ECLIPSE

A Literary Journal

D0126369

Volume Twenty Fall 2009
Glendale Community College
Glendale, California

ECLIPSE
A Literary Journal

EDITOR	Bart Edelman
FICTION EDITOR	Michael Ritterbrown
FICTION READERS	Mara Beckett Deirdre Mendoza
	Ara Corbett Chris Pasles
	Denise Ezell Piper Rooney
	Rosemary Kwa William Rosenblatt
	Kate Martin Rowe Shant Shahoian
POETRY EDITOR	Bart Edelman
EDITORIAL ASSISTANTS	Elena Grigorian
	Arin Keshishian
	Vicki Vasquez
BOOK DESIGN	Susan Cisco
COVER DESIGN	Greg Parks
COVER ART	Norman Lundin
	The Music Room, 2008
	Oil on canvas, 36" x 66"
	Koplin Del Rio Gallery
	Culver City, California

Eclipse thanks the Associated Students of Glendale Community College, Stuart Riddle and Melita Bauman Riddle for their generous grants. We also wish to express our gratitude to Audre Levy, Dawn Lindsay, Larry Serot, Kristin Bruno, Monette Tiernan, Hbuk Bayer and Susan Cisco for their support.

Eclipse is a literary journal published annually at Glendale Community College. The editors invite submissions of poetry and fiction. Manuscripts will be returned only if accompanied by a self-addressed, stamped envelope. Sample issues are $8.

Printed by McNaughton and Gunn, Saline, Michigan.

Glendale Community College
1500 North Verdugo Road
Glendale, California 91208

eclipse@glendale.edu

ISSN 1530-5066

ISBN 0-9701938-9-0

CONTENTS

Donna Pucciani/**Wind Quintet**

Enter the music
like Alice down the rabbit hole.
Land somewhere in the clarinet's ebony
between reed and bell.

Slide into ivory,
rest your head on the pillow of keys.
Taste the tongues of silver flutes.
Disappear into the bassoon's brown-throated
thrush, her deep wings a minuet to morning.

A rabbit buries her head in a clump
of clover as the shadow of an oboe
engulfs her inch by inch, and hedgehogs sing.

How is this sound written in black and white,
where jot turns to dance a trill away
from nowhere, and you balance yourself
on the edge of sunrise?

Donna Pucciani/Mary McGuire

Plump and fresh as a scone warm from the oven,
Mary absorbs the identity of short pastry
through the palms of her hands.
Her doughy bosom rises like twin cupcakes
floury and white beneath her tea-cloth dress
covered in roses.

She smells of butter and jam and clotted cream.
The rolling pin, with its red-painted handles,
becomes an extension of her pale English arms
as, pie-eyed and smiling, she presses
the unbaked crust to the counter,
then crimps the edges on a glass plate,
her hair the color of Pillsbury,
her apron dusted with bleached wheat.

Four and twenty blackbirds flap overhead.
Woman becomes biscuit.

Susan Howard Case/Departure

My husband never intruded until he left.
He was a quiet part of the copper beech
and the red-winged blackbirds by the pond.

Now he shouts his way into my mind
shoving aside what I wanted to say
something about tables and chairs

that assert a life of their own
and about the way the sound of rain
is always the same. I don't know

where any of that would go,
because here he is blocking my view.
I'm ready to do battle, to make him

become what I don't want,
what he really is, a tired, aging man
who likes to sit at home

drinking, thinking his old thoughts.
I want tables, chairs, rain.
I want the copper beech and blackbirds.

I want him gone.

Jeffrey Talmadge/Other Life

We were that house
you could see from the highway,
far enough away
you couldn't tell who we were.

A small house
in the middle of a large field.
It was fall,
right after the trees were bare
but before all signs of life
were gone.

We stood in the backyard and watched
as the geese flew over.
We lay on a blanket at night,
counting meteors, considering
how small we were.

We had clothes hanging out to dry,
mostly white things like sheets and underwear
and unstarched shirts,
because we liked the way
they sounded when the wind blew
and how they smelled when we took them in.

We hoped a baby was on the way.
We talked about getting old.

We wondered if our friends would find us.
Cars hummed in the distance.
We didn't wonder who they were
or where they were going.

Jeffrey Talmadge/The Man Who Left Like Rimbaud

Happily lost in an unknown town,
I know for that moment
that if I wanted, I could disappear.

And in that moment
I see someone I once knew,
who left home
in the middle of the night
and became, like Rimbaud,
famous for disappearing.

The years of drugs and dodging creditors
didn't so much make him mean
as just someone who had
years of drugs and dodging creditors.

Some said genius, some said thief,
and he had no answer.
Some are quiet
when they have said
all that needs to be said
and some are quiet
only when everyone quits listening.

Hari Bhajan Khalsa/Spell #11

Climb the wall. You are egg white, shell, yolk—
a hatched thing, tumbled out, rolled. The fall could kill.

Press the pain: index finger into thigh, pad of thumb jammed
in the arch of your left foot, fist between the brows. Don't say a word.

Don't go back to bed. Sit up. Wrestle. Mind/spirit/mind. . . Parrots:
   emerald,
squawking, wheeling, don't give a crap for contracts, annuities, the
   dotted

line. Rub it all over you—eternity. Like castor, it's good but tastes like
hell. You have a stomach; let it churn, sea waves, torrents. Stroke

the beastly. Utter: tomorrow, lotus roots in mud, first caress.

Take out a pen. In the margins write your way out of town.
Don't say you didn't ask for your life. Take it and run.

Hari Bhajan Khalsa/Spell #66

Go back to when you were ten. No, better—seven.
Shutter the years ahead.
Don't look at them.

Summer is the potion.
Draw the days like train tracks.
The world is two blocks wide and four blocks long.

You are wearing clothes your Aunt May gave you.
You want to be a boy.
You want to fly.

You know that both are possible,
taste your dusty hair, crabapples,
say to yourself: cotton, scabs, mud on a stick.

Look into the canyon.
In the lava you find remnants, pages.
Call up the shimmer of sweat, hush of chamomile.

Circle the willow in the neighbor's yard.
Your toes barely touch the ground.
Your mother's calling, *Dinner.*

Focus on the painted porch.
Take another sip.
When you hear the hoofbeats, cross the mountains.

Settle on a twisted branch.
Let the wind hit.
Swallow clouds.

Wait for your echo.
Echo back
the blue of your feathers.

Susana H. Case/Ephemera

He says that in the dark we feel the same
—his dead wife and me; cleft

to me, I think he means not the waxed weight
and heft of her, but the whispery

memory. I imagine
the razor-cut vein, the schism of skin,

one hundred Seconals swallowed, scattered
on the perfect terra cotta floor with her.

Or maybe it happened a different way.
Of course I cannot ask.

From the closet's cedar boxiness, I try
on her soft black napa jacket

to see if what he says is true, that we
are sized like twins. A second skin, a suffocation

of the one beneath—the fit so like a body bag.
It will be years before I can afford

to buy myself a jacket like this. When he too
will be susurrus, ghost of a synapse, grist.

Mary R. Estrada/The Leaden Hour

I know a place to shun the leaden hour;
The path was found in pain's profound nadir.
When life endures so little offers power.

They came and prayed and sang their hymns most dour—
I knew not hope nor song nor friend, just tears.
I know a place to shun the leaden hour.

To live is like a grave that grows no flower,
Each day you seek to make more reasons clear;
When you endure so little offers power.

With sips, then gulps of grief, you taste the sour;
All days remain like dreaded spectral spheres—
I know a place to shun the leaden hour.

My cradle rocked your early life as bower;
Now speak to me, your sleep transcends my fear.
When life endures we're left with little power.

As demons of remembrance stay devoured,
I teach myself to make my soul austere.
I know a place to shun the leaden hour;
When life endures so little leaves us power.

Aaron Hellem/San Raphael

I saw a dead dog on the side of the street, and it derailed my day in ways that seeing a dead rattlesnake or a dead rodent wouldn't have. It made me stop, look twice to make sure it really was what I thought it was, and when I was sure it was a dead dog I'd seen it twice. The way the eyes were opened wide, flies buzzing around and landing right on them, sticky but no longer wet. The mouth still grinning. The tongue hung off to the side, limp and purple. The side of it covered with dirt and gravel.

It made me talk to myself to try and forget the image of it during the long walk to work. What the dead dog made me realize as I stepped over cracks in the concrete was that everything was always moving in one direction: if not forwards, then it was moving backwards.

The foreman said, You're late, and I told him it was the dead dog I saw. Did you kill it? the foreman said. His was the type of mouth you never saw move. His mustache did all his talking.

No, I told him. I didn't kill it. I just saw it. On the side of the road.

Then how the hell did it make you late? he said. I just don't get it, if you didn't kill it and it was already dead, then how in hell did it keep you from getting here on time? He stood there smug behind his clipboard and his short-sleeved dress shirt, his thick mustache and clip-on tie. What he didn't get was there was no way I could feel any worse about it. I didn't say anything when I walked out, I just walked out and dropped my helmet in a garbage can and stood there on the curb amazed that it was that easy, and I never had to go back there again.

With nowhere to go, I went into the nearest watering hole and told the girl behind the bar to pour me a glass of the coldest beer. I just quit my job, I told her. She poured me the beer, but didn't say anything. That's not the reason for the beer though, I said.

Three dollars, she said.

I wasn't supposed to be in bars per my probation and wasn't supposed to be drinking because of those meetings and the twelve steps. The first sip was always the most bitter, but always the coldest. I gave the girl five. I'll be quiet if you keep them coming, I told her.

She didn't laugh. She wasn't going to ask me why I was drinking at ten in the morning or wonder if I didn't have better places to be. She'd pay me as much mind as she would a dead dog lying on the side of the road.

The real reason I'm drinking a beer this early is because I saw a dead dog on the side of the road today, on my way walking to the job I just quit, I told her.

She listened. She seemed to understand what it meant, why I needed a beer because of it and why I'd quit a perfectly good job over it. Why were you walking? she said.

They took away my license, I told her. The word they used was revoked, which probably meant for good.

She nodded.

The dog was yellow, I told her.

Was it hit by a car? She stood closer to me.

There wasn't any blood.

She nodded like she knew what that meant. I'd quit too if I saw that, she said.

The truth was I'd quit jobs for reasons less severe than that, sometimes just because having to go to work would get in the way of drinking during the day.

She said, My boyfriend died two days ago. She said it without crying.

How old was he?

He was two years older than me, she said.

Car accident? Knife stab? Rare cancer? Suicide?

He got a staph infection, she said.

I had no idea what that meant, or how in the world it could kill someone.

From a tattoo, she said.

I have a tattoo, I told her, never realizing it could've killed me in any way. I lifted up my shirt sleeve and showed her: a snake wound around an iron cross.

Me, too, she said. She turned around and pulled her shirt and bra strap off her shoulder, showed me a rising angel with wings outspread, floating above her shoulder blade. The blue ink made the wings look like smoke and the face surly. We got them together, she said.

I slid my glass towards her, nodded for her to have some, that she had as good a reason as anybody else. She stared down at the glass, the bubbles popping, the bubbles rising up to the top. That's a good reason to quit a job, I told her. I tried to think how it would be to fall in love with someone and then have them die on me like that. She started crying, hard little tears she squeezed out her eyes like diamonds.

It's never going to feel good again, she said.

I didn't know what to tell her. Maybe, I said.

She reached behind the bar and grabbed her purse. I didn't ask her where she was going. I watched her walk out the door in the mirror behind the bottles: the way the door opened up like a mouth and swallowed her in daylight, and the way the door closed shut with a slam and it was dark again. Bar dark where you couldn't ever tell what time of day it was.

When I finished the beer, I walked around to the other side, washed the glass, and took up an apron. When a couple of guys came in for a lunch-time beer, I served them up like it was what I'd always done, like I had never worked construction at all, like I didn't start off the day seeing a dead dog and quitting my job.

I wiped things down and opened fresh bottles of whatever was empty. When everyone cleared out, it was lonely. I kept thinking about the dog. The freezer hummed, and traffic beeped. I tried to think of other things besides the dog and the girl crying. Outside the sun was hot and the dust thick, but in California the sun was always hot and the dust was always thick. I bet there wasn't any dust in Alaska.

I went into the back where the bathrooms were. I pushed the ladies' room door open. I pictured her in there before I came in, sitting in one of the stalls crying quiet to herself. Choking on it getting bigger inside her chest, the way that kind of sadness grew wings and spread them out. The way it encroached on her lungs. Maybe she had to hold on to the sink to keep herself standing up. Ran the water so nobody would hear. I thought about the tattoo that killed her boyfriend. It must've been big or had lots of color. I looked at mine in the mirror. Traced my fingers over it. What did it feel like? I got it in Sacramento when I still had my driver's license. I listened to my pulse to see if it was poisoned. It was, but not bad enough to kill me outright.

Regulars showed up and started asking after her. I told some of them I didn't know anything. Told others she was on vacation. Then I told them she was looking after her sick mother. They believed it because we all had mothers, and they got sick eventually. My relief showed up at four. Where's Rita? he said.

How the hell should I know? I told him. I stayed there behind the bar.

He clocked in and opened an envelope with cash in it. Did Ritchie hire you on? he said. That's Ritchie for you, always hiring and firing without word one. This guy Doug who used to work here didn't even know he was fired until he showed up and his shift was filled. He stood there watching me.

What do I do now? I asked him.

Go home, he said. Or go get drunk yourself. I don't care.

I asked him if he knew where Rita lived because there were tips left over for her, and I could drop them off on my way. He believed me and told me where it was. I had one for the road because the road would be dry and dusty.

Rita lived in an apartment building a few blocks away from the bar. I watched it from the street. Scanned the third floor windows for hers. I tried to guess which one it was from the curtain colors, but I didn't have to because there she was, standing in the frame of it smoking. In her underwear, skinnier than she'd looked that morning. Her belly extra white and her hair bright red in the daylight. Her long face yellow like she was getting ready to die herself. Her sunk eyes dripping farther down her face. She looked ready to spin herself backwards, back to a place of crawling and crying. She looked all set to be a fish again. She'd cut her hair and her forearm. I saw the thick gauze wrapped around it. An accident then, if she dressed it herself. Or, maybe, a change of heart. She sagged in the window like somebody had spilled her there. She moved away from it, and a few minutes later came out the downstairs door. She was in a bathrobe and sandals. She went down the sidewalk and limped over the cracks in the concrete. The bathrobe was too big for her. The sandals made soft prints in the dust. I stayed behind and didn't say anything to her. She would've looked into my face and nodded, yes, she remembered me from earlier, but would've only seen her boyfriend's dark eyes and cleft chin. His strong edges and black stubble. The scar above his eye where a biker punched a slash there with a set of car keys.

She went down to the corner into a store for a cup of coffee and a fresh pack of cigarettes. I watched from the window, and then went in when she left. I asked the clerk why she didn't pay him. He didn't know what to say. I told him I had money and wanted to pay for what she bought. A cup of coffee and a pack of Winstons. She didn't give you any money, I said.

She doesn't have to, he said. He reached under the counter and kept his hand there. I thought he might be fingering a gun.

Why not? I said.

Who the hell are you? he said.

I tried to think quick, but I've never been good on my feet. Her brother, I said.

She doesn't have a brother.

I was stuck. He started pushing a button down there. All right, I said.

Then he said, I'm calling the cops.

I stood still.

Right now, he said. He kept pushing the button.

I ran. Out the store and around the corner and down the street, and I kept running until I knew I was out of sight.

My second day on the job I poured drinks without thinking. I didn't even check the letters on the liquor gun. I pressed any of them, sometimes a little of each, and served up glasses full of multicolored whatevers the regulars pounded without complaint. They stopped asking about Rita, but I kept thinking about her. Kept seeing her in that window and the long sad smoke coming out of her.

One of the regulars came in with a dog. It followed him inside ragged like a beggar kid. Head down, belly swollen, tail dragging. It was so dirty and starved that I couldn't even tell what kind it was. The owner didn't have a leash for it, and it probably had fleas or mites. He came towards the bar, but I held up a hand and stopped him. The dog lay down at his feet. He had on two different shoes and a woman's blouse with the buttons on the wrong side.

You can't bring that dog in here, I told him. I laid down the law, and the dog licked at the floor.

Where's Rita? he said. Rita always lets me. His body bent like a re-used nail.

Rita's not here, I told him.

She's not? he said. He didn't know where to put his hands. I could see they were shaking, and I knew what that meant. Sores around his mouth. His eyes caved into his head like potholes. But Rita always lets me, he said again.

Rita's not here anymore, I told him. The dog stays outside.

He looked down at the mutt, and then led it back towards the door. He propped the door open with his shoe, and forced the dog's backside down to make it sit on the ground. You can't, he said, and I heard the dog whimper. I know, I heard him say, but you can't. The dog licked at the fronts of its paws and then licked the ground in front of it. All of its bones poked through its loose skin. The owner came back in and sat down at the bar. She doesn't cause any harm, he said.

It's the health code, I told him, though that had nothing to do with it, or if it did, I didn't know it. You can't have animals in a restaurant, I said.

This is a bar, he said.

We still serve food, I told him. I pointed at the cashew dispenser and the olives in the garnish dish.

That doesn't seem hardly fair, he said.

I didn't want to argue about it anymore. What do you want? I said.

He reached into his pockets and unloaded a pile of change.

Are you kidding me? I said.

It's money, he said.

His dog moaned low from the door. An El Camino with mariachi blowing out the sides sped by and peeled around the corner. The dog was so deaf from hunger that it didn't hear it.

Fine, I said.

Rita gives me whiskey, he said.

I gave him a shot and he counted out enough change for it. He knew how much it cost. I had no idea what they charged for drinks. He leaned over and sipped off the top. Then he sipped a little more until it was low enough for him to pick up without spilling any. He looked over his shoulder at the dog. The dog whined.

That dog needs food, I told him.

I don't have any money for that.

You have money to get drunk though.

I'm taking her over to the Mexican restaurant, he said.

You feed your dog Mexican food?

Whatever we find in the dumpsters. He was one hundred percent serious. I wished for enough whiskey to douse him and make him disappear and take his dog home. Give her some Chuck Wagon and beef bones. Let her fill out her skin back to normal.

I should kill you both, I told him, and I was one hundred percent serious. Put both of them out of the misery of their hunger and thirst.

Why does she have to lick the dirt like that? he said.

She's hungry, I told him. She wants food, and she'll keep on licking the dirt until she gets some. What about you, you piece of shit? Do you want anything that bad?

He nodded. I want another whiskey, he said. I have the money. He pointed at his pile of change.

That's what I figured.

Because the bar was in a rougher part of town, I knew there'd be a pistol tucked somewhere behind the bar, and it was there when I reached for it, in a holster under the cash register. I slid it out and went towards the door. Nobody said anything to me. I walked right up to the dog. She didn't get up. She shrank back into her bones to hide behind her skin. Her eyes looked up at me. She moaned from the bottom of her. Shifted in the dust. Licked at the ground. I slid a bullet into the chamber and flipped off the safety. I pressed the barrel against her head. She whimpered, and I pulled the trigger. The gun kicked back and vibrated up my arm. Her body rolled backwards and bled bright red into the rusty dirt. Her legs twitched, and her lungs kept pumping. I went back in and closed the door. The gun felt hot in my grip. My chest was on fire. I went behind the bar and slapped the pistol down on top of it. I spun it, and it circled around and banged against the bar like someone knocking. We all watched it quietly spin out to a stop. When it did, it was pointed at me.

I wish you hadn't done that, the owner said.

Then have your revenge, I said, and nodded at the gun between us, already aimed at me so all he had to do was grab the handle and pull the trigger.

He sweated down the sides of his face.

Shouldn't we call someone? one of the other flies said. Nobody answered him.

He wanted whiskey more than he wanted me dead.

That's what I thought, I said. I should've picked up the pistol and pressed the barrel against his forehead to vent out the back of his head. I felt the crying come up in me.

Just give me a whiskey, he said. His eyes wouldn't look up. Please, he said.

I left him there wanting, the pistol still warm on the bar. Left the bar in its timelessness and out into the brightness of the streets. The cry came out before I got to the corner. It pounded inside my chest and forced me to my knees. Everyone around me thought I was choking. A large man in a necktie sweating puddles through his shirt got behind me and did the Heimlich. His fat hands stuck into my sternum, and I felt my ribs cave in because he was too high and doing it all wrong. The tears came out in streams every time he heaved.

Come on, he grunted, and thrust. It was stuck down there in my stomach wrapped in barbed wire. It was kicking and ripping at me. Too big to come up my chest the normal way. The fat man lifted me off my knees and heaved and pushed his hands into me, and his sweat burned like hot rain when it dripped on me. I coughed and collapsed onto the sidewalk. I felt it shake me from the inside. I heard them panic and someone run to call an ambulance. I rolled over on my back. Opened my eyes and the blue sky hurt. It was eclipsed by the dark outline of the fat man's face coming down to kiss me.

No! I shouted at him. Stopped him with my hands. He sat there with his fat mouth half opened. The rest of them stood around me in a circle. It poured out of me and burst out my eyes, and my mouth and my nose, rushed out like a spitting hydrant. They all stepped back, and the fat man fell backwards on his ass and then scooted farther away when I shook and kicked and swore. I sat up and everyone watched me. Traffic had stopped to stare. The dust was settled. The day was still. Sirens struck through it and sliced it in half. I got up and blinked at them. They held their hands out ready to catch me though they all looked terrified to touch me.

I'm all right, I told them. I started down the sidewalk, and they parted a path for me. My feet shuffled, and my legs broke into strides, and I ran while sirens chased me.

I stood across the street from her apartment and watched her in the window. Her eyes dark shotgun holes. I waited until she left to go down to the corner store, and I went inside and up the stairs to her apartment. The peephole was a portal below 3E. I turned the knob knowing it wouldn't be locked. How did I know that? There was a burning in my forearms that told me I wouldn't have to break it down.

Something in the kitchen smelled like fish. There were more ashtrays than I could count. All of them puking out butts from their wide mouths. Clothes were piled along the walls. Dishes stacked on the counters. Garbage in the sink. In the living room, towels and tissues and newspapers had exploded all around a spot cleared in the center where she probably sat and cried until she fell asleep. The furniture was covered with men's clothes and photographs and a pair of boots and a leather jacket. One of the pictures was of her on his lap kissing his cheek, and he was looking at the camera with his eyebrows raised, his whole face smiling, happy and sure he'd never die. The walls were a memorial of him in different moments of living: dancing close to her, carrying her across a bridge, riding his motorcycle, sleeping against a tree. I felt his presence there wondering what the hell I was doing. Don't know, I said out loud.

Upstairs, a tea kettle whistled. Outside, two cars honked at each other. He was probably a man with the kind of confidence that didn't ever need a knife or a gun. Could take care of anything with his hands. I stood in front of the photograph of him standing by a campfire with his head cocked back and his arms crossed, a cigarette between his lips. I stuck out my hand. Shake it, I said. I've got strong hands, too. I held it out there, and he just stared at me from the past. The world on his terms. He had San Raphael tamed to follow him without a leash.

I went into the bathroom and switched on the light. The face in the mirror belonged to a bona fide piece of shoe crud who was born to leave everything he touched in ashes. The eyes hunger-hollow. The jaw a piece of jagged metal. He had a tattoo on his bicep that could've killed him, and he never even knew it. His nose red and swollen. Who are you? I asked him.

He smiled at me.

I stuck out my hand. Shake it, I told him.

He stuck out his hand, but they didn't reach.

I opened the mirror and inside were her bottles of pills and her make up and toothbrush. I read the labels on the pill bottles. Twice daily. Two at night. Two in the morning. I grabbed her mascara. I dipped the brush into it and then brushed my lashes with it. I did it once and then twice. I opened the blush compact and dabbed the rosy orange on my cheeks. Then I pinched them. I'd heard that's how it was done. I pinched them again. Then grabbed the red lipstick. I pressed it against my bottom lip. Slick like wet asphalt after a quick heavy rain and a few too many. They glowed like cherry bleeds. I'd seen women kiss tissue, but I kissed the glass. I leaned in and pressed my lip-sticked kisser against the cold glass. It kissed me back, but it wasn't warm or comforting. I stuck out my tongue, and it was rancid grey. It was enough to make me cry, and then I finally did. Hard tears dripped burning cold down my cheeks and smeared the mascara. Black streaks muddied with the blush. Black wet streaks like tire treads around a corner where the road bent. Then I heard the door open and close. I held my breath, and then she appeared in the mirror in front of me when she stood behind me. I thought she was going to scream. Or run. She stood there behind me and looked at my face in the mirror. She reached out and put her hand on my shoulder, and it was so warm I thought I was going to melt. She was crying, too, hers making red streaks. She didn't ask me what I was doing there.

I'm sorry about your dog, she said. She disappeared from the mirror, and I listened to her go into the living room. The crumple of newspapers under her bare feet. I heard her light a cigarette. I ran the water and rubbed off the black streaks. The red lips. My eyes looked back at me dark and empty as barrels.

She was standing by the window. The smoke was clouding up the room. Her body looked deflated in her underpants. The straps on her bra thing slid off her shoulders, and she let them. The angel on her back was blue as a bruise. How many nights had she stayed up thinking about how it could've killed her? How many times had she wished it did? I didn't even know his name, and it didn't matter then. I didn't want to know it.

Don't you have any family you can call? I asked her. I could see the bones in her shoulder and all the ones down her back. I don't know why I said that, I said. I don't have anybody to call. I couldn't see her face. Her hair was dirty. Then I saw that all of her was dirty. I went back into the bathroom and ran the hot water and filled the bathtub.

Come on, I told her. She came over to me, and I wrapped my arms around her. She was cold, and her sadness didn't make a sound. I could feel in her skin how much she wanted it to end. For it to just be over with. I led her into the bathroom, and she stood there while I took off her bra thing and slipped down her underpants, and she held onto my shoulder while she stepped each foot out of them. I helped her into the tub, and she eased down into the hot water. I told her to get all the way down in it. That it would feel better. She dipped her head in and held it under for a long time. I tapped on her knee, and she came back up. Water dripped from her hair down her face and her neck and her chest. I soaped up a washcloth and rubbed it across her shoulders and neck. She stuck out her arms, and I rubbed all the way down them. I felt her bones shaking inside her fingers and hands and shoulders. Somewhere upstairs in another apartment a television was blaring gunshots and squealing tires. I ran more hot water into the tub and rubbed the washcloth down her legs. I held her feet against my chest and washed them with slow circles. Her eyes were closed. Her lips were moving. I rubbed the soft bottoms of them and in between her toes. Up the tops of them and around her ankles. She was singing. And then she was sobbing. I leaned her forward and rubbed down her back. She put her chin on her knees, and her spine stuck out like scales. I rubbed each one and then along the sides and her shoulder blades. I rubbed the blue out of her guardian angel and washed the cobwebs out of her wings. It looked pink and born again. I rubbed up her neck and watched how the guardian angel watched me and my hands. It was all the faith and comfort we had left, the useless idols painted on our skin.

Teresa Breeden/I Wouldn't Mind

having the kind of walk
that stops traffic
or a Nobel-winning intellect, wouldn't
mind receiving that sweepstakes
notification, or placing first
in every contest.
I wouldn't mind
if everything I think I want
comes to pass.

Barring that, I don't mind
pressing my body
into service before the sun:
waking in a cool room,
cooking breakfast for two
and a half, gathering by the fireplace, and all
before day clocks in.

Or the way my husband smoothes
my hair
absentmindedly,
warm hands, soft eyes:
a wanderer who doesn't hate this home.
And later, the moment I lose myself in sleep,
dropping toward eternity.

I don't mind the learning that happens
every day, or the teaching. And
my son's two baby teeth strike me
as quite a prize.

Neither do I mind dust on my car
from the high desert winds, nor the
traffic light that is always red.

There is time at a red light for contemplating
the honesty of not winning everything,
for realizing the mess
stopped traffic would make,
and remembering that the most likely way
to win a sweepstakes
is inheritance and for that,
someone I love
has to die.

Teresa Breeden/Lament

My cat has two more paws
than I, and his are furrier.
Also, I lack whiskers
to test the air. It's a wonder
I don't run into walls and doors,
a wonder I can even hold my head level.
And what's this? No tail?
My body slumps to one side then
the other, no third or fifth point
of balance, nothing to wag,
and I am, of course, shivering,
sad bald creature, worn out
from the lack of good things:
no fur tufts in my ears, no retractable
claws, not even enough flexibility
to lick my own butt.
Ah me, how cheerless life is,
ungainly and pale, devoid
of feral qualities, wishing
I could, at the least,
unhinge my jaw
just a little.

Lewis S. Keith/Two Cigars and a Lie or Two

We sat around the arbor, two of us smoking cigars, talking about Lubbock history, give or take a lie or two, which meant I kept my mouth shut and listened. Three of us would be smoking cigars, but one decrepit senior was on antibiotics, and his doctor explicitly forbade smoking. Unlike the other old codgers who lived decades in Lubbock, I retired to Carillon from elsewhere. Pappy was a geologist, tottering, but ambulatory, and still articulate; Frank & Frank were schoolteachers; one with palsy, the other damned with optic atrophy; Doc still earns a few dollars interpreting x-ray photos for a bankrupt hospital, though lately pay is sporadic.

One of the Franks finished a story about offspring of the mansions once known as "Bootlegger's Row," and launched into an estimate of costs of additions to one of the mansions at either 34th or 19th, and Canton Street. Everyone immediately identified the house, except me. I have a hazy idea of its location, for Lubbock is laid out on a grid, with east/west streets numbered numerically, and north/south streets named alphabetically. This particular Frank dabbled in Lubbock realty for half a century, and has intricate, intimate knowledge of particular parcels, and shared knowledge and gossip concerning foibles of their owners.

The names of characters of their stories have no meaning to me, though Doc and the Franks can recite offspring and scandals of particular families in detail for three or four generations. One of the wonders is how Carillon keeps appearing in the fabric: an aunt came to Carillon twenty-five years ago, and so, of course, her daughter and niece came ten years later. The place is riddled with cousins and marriage-relationships, and I wish I had diagrams to help in understanding why saying something nice about Camellia riles up Lily. Family vines are not confined to Lubbock. Communities within a hundred-mile radius, more or less, are intertwined with Lubbock, frequently through family-owned ranches, banks, or department stores. "He married the widow, and the family voted him into the chairmanship about a year later, and. . ."

All are grist for the mill of these chroniclers of a time already shrouded in mist. All the blemishes, all the frailties, making stories worth retelling are dust. But for a moment, for an instant of resurrection, a shadow of another time, another place, lives on in our imaginations.

Fall is early this year, and evenings are cool. The coats of animals are thicker, and rainfall this year already exceeds 18 inches. Crops are bountiful, so area farmers, thanks to price supports and world markets, will earn more millions. We gather at the arbor on the East side, and two of us smoke cigars. Talk turns to events in Lubbock history, give or take a lie or two, and I listen.

Gayle Jansen Beede/My Brother Chopping Wood

I had become the Tin Man.
What oils me is the memory
of my brother chopping wood—
his fierce, unswaying focus
in the half-light of dusk.
He was only twelve,
but Dad trusted him with the axe.
A stack of kindling
in no time flat,
fragrant splinters flying,
an audience of Steller's Jays & me.
From across the campsite
I watched, diary on my lap,
jotting names of titan trees:
Father of the Forest,
Mother and Son,
The Three Graces.
I sketched knots of muscle
in his branch-like arms.
Now, we've sawn through middle age.
A hundred miles apart.

When we visit, we build a fire
with store-bought logs.

We don't talk about the storms
brewing in one another—
like rings in a tree trunk,
they tell of survival.
Safer, now, to take note
of what we've passed down

to children who look
to us for answers,
limbs to hang onto.

Gayle Jansen Beede/Fortunate

In the photograph
I'm pushing sixteen.
My father shot it
from the doorway,
never saying *cheese*,
hesitant to enter
my bedroom back then.

I sit on the floor
at the foot of the bed,
my mother's hand-me-down
Smith Corona balanced
on my knees. A lace ribbon
holds my hair back.
I wear a T-shirt and jeans

and don't appear ashamed
of the pimples on my chin.
My lousy fear of death
had not yet set in.
I'm a mere two years
into periods, a rookie
at cramps and mood swings.

In another country
a girl my age might need to haul
buckets of water on her head.
At night, she'd collapse
hungry into a tent,
whisking away mosquitoes
with sweaty, blistered hands.

She might not know
the thrill of a clean sheet

of paper fed securely
around the roller on a cozy
winter night that invites poetry over
like a good friend in PJs.

Chances are she could not
identify the words of cummings
or Carver or Sexton or Frost
if you paid her in gold.

She wouldn't know the muse
if it barged its way in with a bayonet.

Richard Robbins/In the Foothills

What Blackfeet call the backbone of the world
lies still behind me, its most recent snow
melting by day, halfway to the foothills
by the time north-flying cranes settle down

for evening, by the time the last loud car
finds its way home. If I were the body
for that spine, hand and mouth for skittish birds
crossing a cold marsh, how would this body

answer mind, and what greater thing beyond
this skin would make the call easy as a dream
sent by ancestors, or the shape of wind?
What would that intelligence have me say
and do, my car in the stall, the broad sweep
of sky waiting for something to save us.

Richard Robbins/Home Before Three

If he hadn't come home that afternoon,
he would not have seen the kitchen without
its brain or closets in distress. Whole rooms
waited on their lawn as she chipped paint, grout

to get inside a wall, to shine her own
brand of doubt on each stud and junction box,
a copper hum bleeding to air, a song
they sang once, happily enough, in dark.

He was as surprised, finally, as her
to love the wreck of their life in small parts,
leaked to the street, as neighbors, like yesterday,
wondered how they had strayed, such a nice house,
even as the two turned from it, made new vows,
walked naked as on the first day away.

Mary Bass Poulin/For Sale

Things that leave: trees, parents,
memory, muscle, old dogs,
children, my old red plow.
The truck we stuck
with a For Sale sign at the end of the road
next to the highway—
gotta love Yankee shoppers:
sold: one day.
I was sad to see it go—
yesterday,

I am going to the mountain to plow—
no babysitter today—the boys next
to me, their little boot-stuffed feet jutting
out, knees straight. Ninja Turtles, juice boxes,
pirate figures, animal crackers, fruit
rollups clutter their laps and the truck floor.
We rock for hours, we three, in the old truck.
Things that leave: a young family, Little
League, life preservers, nightlights, bedtime tales.
Have you heard the joke: what do you get when
you play country and western songs backward?
You get your wife back, your dog back, your truck
back. It actually doesn't work; I tried.
Things that stay: don't know—the declaration
of independence? Maybe love? Or not?

John Brantingham/Papa in Space

The void has no time, no past, no future.
It's only objects that age,
decay, and die. Hemingway
had it wrong I think.
He sent his people to cold places
to find the end of atrophy,
up to Kilimanjaro or Switzerland,
but he should have written SciFi—
should have put his wounded heroes
in spaceships and shot them up
to a place where no child dies,
where no one stinks of gangrene,
where babies aren't aborted,
where Indians don't slit their own throats.

Rolf Yngve/Billy

The way it is with Caroline, someone gets the blame. She's Catholic; blame seems a natural part of any untidy event. Without blame, how can you decide whether or not to forgive? It's in her nature, find those who need absolution. That's all. They will be healed. So looking for someone to blame was easy enough for her when the neighbor's poodle killed Billy.

For me, it isn't so easy, finding blame. There are always questions, reasons and disorder, acts of commission and omission. I am never so certain.

The way I see it, you can't blame the dog. The dog was big, the cat stupid. Just because the dog had a fancy haircut didn't mean he wasn't going to do what dogs do. He didn't have to stop to think, Let's see now. Stop and go about my business or chase the cat? I'm sure he was a little surprised when he caught him. But I'm also sure he didn't have to mull it over, think something like, Now what do I do? Maybe I'll give it a little tooth and see what happens.

I figure, the dog ran over, all billowy white and perky, gave Billy a shake and that was it. Except for the part where the cat finished himself off running with a broken back.

I didn't see any of this. Even if I had seen it, I'm pretty sure I wouldn't have been able to prevent it. These things happen quickly, you blink and it's over, a second of inattention and all you can do is pick up the pieces. Dogs are good at what they do. They're bred to it.

What happened—the cat just went missing. He usually comes in at night. But that Saturday he didn't return. He was a big cat, friendly. But like I say, he was stupid. We called him Billy after a general I once worked for, also big, friendly and stupid.

At first, when he was only missing, Caroline wasn't all that concerned. He was gone, absent, doing things but coming back. Deployed like any of us do. Away, but returning. A fact of life. At the worst, a little slip up. Like she said, we should have kept him in the house.

It would have been tough, though. The doors are always open out to the back. The sun warms up every day after it works through the marine layer. Billy liked to sit out in the garden, rest on raw dirt, put his nose up and breathe in that ocean air tinged with the snappy smell tomatoes get in the sun. Hummingbirds would drop down, a yard from his nose to talk about him, bitch him out. The birds interested him but nobody had ever showed him they were anything better than the stuff that came out of the can. Billy took a crack at catching them. But they were way too quick, too alert. Finally, he gave up. He would keep his head down on his paws, napping, ignoring these birds confounding him.

That's where we left him, last time we saw him, sunning himself in the back while we went to vigil. No blame in that.

We like going to Mass Saturday evenings. The vigil is never crowded. People we know fill the pews far enough apart to be comfortable, close enough to wave hello. Often, Caroline leans into me on the pew, puts her arm around me, holds me close to her. There, I'm calm with her soft scent and firm arm, oblivious to any liturgy. Me and Billy, basking.

Losing that moment is what I worry about most deployed. There's no wonder in this. It's a hard life, but not like most people think. It isn't as if you spend day after day immersed in violence, one horrific assault after another. Nothing like that.

For me, it's the anticipation that wears me out. Given six, eight or twelve months in charge of twenty, then a hundred, then a thousand young men and women, there are moments, instances, to make you dread the next knock on your door. And it always comes, that knock. And it's never good news. They save the good news for staff meetings and commanders' conferences. Bad news comes to you fast, with the same grim report, the same terse words, it seems always at night.

But if I can return to Caroline's arm around me, I let go. It's her acceptance, her warmth, her trust and the simple feeling she cares about me. To feel I've earned it—that care—and can collect. That's what I missed during all those deployments. That's what keeps me breathing sometimes from one moment to the next. She tells me, "You are a good man, Vic. You've done your duty. Now rest."

In the liturgy I say, ". . . I am not worthy to receive you. Only say the word and I shall be healed." Caroline believes that. She believes I deserve that.

When Billy went missing, I made a flyer with his picture on it and started dropping them in mail boxes. I always liked this picture of Billy. He's staring right at the camera and the light caught his eyes so you can see them yellow. He's sitting, his butt huge, head small, and his face blank. It's a blank, confused look on a cat the color of a meatloaf.

The right kind of cat, you can say anything you want to it, call it names, malign its dignity, anything you want and you get the same blank expression. They don't know what's going on. But they don't have to know much of anything. Just enough to run away from a bounding dog. Just enough, like any ambush, the basic thing is to get off the spot. I thought he had at least that much sense, to get off the spot when he sees it coming.

The flyer read, "Billy. Nice but not bright. Missing since Saturday night." Then it gave our address and phone number. It said underneath, "Reward."

The old guy across the street was out letting his dog take its crap when I came by and I asked him if he'd seen our cat. He said no. Then he said that Maurice had a little tussle with a cat the evening before. Maurice was squatting a couple of yards away, the little balls on his trimmed ears dangling with his tongue as he shuddered that turd onto the common property and grinned at us.

I asked him if the cat looked like Billy and held up the flier and the neighbor said yes, he guessed that was the cat. Then I asked him which way the cat ran and he pointed. I said thanks thinking he could have said something to me before; he could have followed the cat. I said thanks understanding how it feels when someone shows up to ask a question you never want asked. I didn't blame him as I said thanks thinking about Maurice eating, shitting and killing.

Creatures, all creatures, generally don't die right away. Most have minutes or hours or days where the machinery shuts down at some rate, more or less gradually, until it fails completely and everything is still. They hang on.

That's the uncomfortable part about learning to hunt or fish. You have to be able to sort of ignore that moment where the game isn't quite dead. The fair-minded will clock a caught fish on the head so it won't suffer too long. The hunting code I learned was you snap a pheasant's neck after the dog brings it up because most times, the shotgun isn't enough to kill it outright. Shoot enough deer and you'll cut one's throat someday to finish it off.

When you're teaching them how to hunt, the trick is teaching them to put their minds in another space during those moments. The first time a child threads a worm on a hook, you say, "Don't worry, the worm can't feel it." The first time a boy shoots a duck from the blind and the dog comes up, you praise his shooting, you exult. Kill your first deer and someone will blood you, maybe, wipe the blood from its cut throat on your cheek so you feel the joy of the moment. It doesn't take much, really, and you'll have them feeling nothing about it one way or another. They don't hear the deer sneeze blood, they don't see the bird rattle its wings inside the dog's mouth, they don't feel the worm wriggle in their fingers. Or, at least, seeing, hearing and feeling those things becomes inconsequential.

On the other side of it, medics talk about that golden hour, that period of time when it's still possible to arrest the dissolution, reach inside to patch the leak, immobilize the broken spine, repair the damage, let them live. Then it becomes consequential. Then the sights, sounds, smells and pulses are exquisitely vital.

We missed Billy the night he was killed. But I didn't go outside to look. Caroline asked, said something about looking for him. Caroline said she might have heard him. Maybe I heard him, too. But Billy had this trick of climbing up on the neighbor's roof then demanding rescue. He would sometimes call to me from some perch in a tree, from inside the garage, from under the car and I'd get up, pad around until I ferreted him out so he could lounge all over our bed, warm and safe. It was as if he would find a place where he depended upon me to come to him, pull him out as if it was some test of love.

I should have gone out to look. I had some wine then some bourbon after mass, keeping that warm glow going, and I was fed up with late night rescues. Caroline was pretty sure she heard him. She said there was a sound, Billy calling she thought, in her sleep or just before. So I looked through the house, called for him.

At least I did that.

Maybe there had been an answer. Maybe I heard something outside. But I didn't get dressed, didn't go out. He was a cat, a night animal, I told myself. He could take care of himself, and I rolled back into the rack and slept off my Saturday next to Caroline, breathing softly. I've learned that. You can't cup them in your hands every minute. You must let them do.

Caroline didn't have much to say to me the next morning. She looked in the closets and cupboards for Billy. Billy was always with her, Billy doesn't deploy. She gets a sharp way of stepping through the house. She gets an edge when something isn't right.

So I looked hard for him, made the flyers first thing, found Maurice and the old man who lets him out. There was no answer when I called and no trace, no blood, no one had seen him, no sign he'd ever been out. I looked up on the roofs, under the porches. Nothing doing.

Caroline was already letting him go, already letting the whole thing get to her, so I looked hard again on Monday after Caroline went to work, called all the vets, all the animal hospitals, talked to the homeowners' association, banged on the neighbor's doors. I found out a lot. Like, the gardeners think they're getting paid too little. The one neighbor's wife had died, and another's husband had left. Kids who used to come by to play with our boys were all gone, grown and beyond, like them.

They found out a lot about me, too. By the time I was done, they knew our boys were doing fine, Caroline had been promoted. They knew I was on terminal leave, finally done. They called me "Colonel" but I say it's just Vic now, and they nodded, satisfied I'd made the shift. I told them I was taking a little break before looking for work. Just a little time off. No responsibility, no worries. By the time I'd made it around the neighborhood, everyone knew I was happy. Everyone knew that when they asked, "So how are things really going over there?" I could only shake my head and say I was glad to be out of it.

They all helped any way they could. But there was no sign of Billy, no golden hour to be found. All the while I thought about Billy bleeding out while I worked off the Jim Beam I'd had before bed.

The last couple years, I've had some pretty bad dreams, had trouble sleeping. Some of these stretch way back, surprising dreams going back thirty-five years, even, back to my first days in the service. Over the years they'd go away then return like unwelcome relatives, knocking the door out of nowhere. Usually not so bad I'd want help. When I'd start awake, Caroline reaches over and we joke about it. She says, "Relatives?"

I'd say, "Worse, in-laws." And we'd roll over.

You don't talk about it with people because they always come up with something like "You should get help with that."

You don't. As long as you're still in, if you want to step up, you suck it up. No help.

Maybe we do better with the young people about that. We're smarter now. But thirty-five years of it for me, and nobody wants to hear about any minor issues like not sleeping well. One of the old dreams snuck in when the cat went missing.

It goes like this: I'm buried in earth wrapped in a wet sheet twisted around my arms and between my legs, pulled over my head, over my eyes, over my nose. I'm breathing through my mouth, through a cardboard tube the size of a toilet paper tube, caught in the dirt, vertical over my lips. I can taste the dirt. Feel the wet sheet with the weight of the earth across my chest.

I don't know where I am. I don't know how deep the soil has been laid over me. I don't know why I'm there. I only know I'm buried.

It feels like I can move a little. I might be so shallow that all I have to do is push, and I'll be able to sit up. Everything will be fine. But if I'm not shallow, if I lose control and start to struggle, I know that cardboard tube balanced over my lips will tilt away, and I'll start to gag and panic with the dirt in my mouth until the wet sheet tightens over my nose, ears, legs, chest, balls, arms, and I'll die like that. Trapped.

So do I wait, hope someone finds me? Or do I try to move, risk the tube falling away?

What I have to do, and the part that makes the nightmare so un-bearable, I have to choke back the panic as long as I can, knowing, in the end, it will have me. It's not only being trapped. It's knowing I'm trapped, knowing I can choose. If only I can maintain control over myself.

I'm sure Billy had no such thoughts when the dog got him. A wounded animal has no responsibility to keep its wits. It only knows to fight back, run. A wounded animal abandons itself to fear and violence.

I suppose that's what the gardener found when he came across Billy, a vicious cat, crazed and wounded. So I don't blame him for using his shovel. These are simple men, these gardeners. They come from the places where you still throw a litter of kittens in a gunny sack and pitch them into a pond because you have no use for them. You find a vicious animal, bloody, hissing and clawing at you under a bush and you use the point of your shovel to take off its head. Then you put it in a plastic bag and throw it in a dumpster. Then, when somebody like me comes around waving a twenty dollar bill, you go get the cat out of the dumpster and bring it to the guy, get your reward.

So I don't blame him. How can you blame him for doing what he does? All he saw was a feral animal, vicious, probably diseased, big and threatening, begging for extermination. I paid him, asked him to take the cat away.

After we found out what happened to Billy, Caroline blamed the old man. There are lots of old men like him in this neighborhood. Most of these guys bought these houses when they were new, in the 70s. The ones who are still here are the ones who never stepped up. They all look the same—some grey hair whipped over the crown or blown up, that pained, shuffling gait. If not using a walker or a cane, they practice how to bend over. Oddly enough, they have wives with different sizes, shapes, colors and dispositions. But these guys, they are all the same, all sour.

So I didn't blame him, either. That dog wasn't his idea. He didn't want to get up every evening and let that bouncy, youthful and plain big animal yank on a leash, trying to make him fall over. He hadn't expected to feel achy and cranky all the time. He hadn't decided to take on the dog. So he did the best he could, and the dog ran out day after day and crapped without anything happening at all until Billy, confounded by hummingbirds, blundered into becoming prey.

I don't see it as his fault. It just happens. Like age. Like the inevitable cane or walker.

Caroline wanted to have the animal control guys come take the dog. "Vicious dog he can't control," she said. "Who knows what would have happened if Billy had been someone's child?"

Dogs like that, I told her, are not wired to kill children. Only cats and other small animals, I told her that it's only natural selection.

"So how many cats do you want him to kill? How many small animals?" This is what Caroline says, and I know it's just grief.

I didn't tell Caroline about opening up the garbage bag with Billy stiff and soiled, stinking the way dead animals do, blood, shit-stained. I told her the gardeners had found him, and he was dead. No sense giving her all the details like the way his eyes were closed, not staring, and how odd it looked with his fur and limbs stiff and twisted by the spade or the garbage where he was buried, who knows which?

That's what you get when something is really dead. After that in between moment, the period while it's dying, it goes completely limp and it falls in ways you can't imagine. All the joints find inappropriate positions. It's no wonder we can't help ourselves from cleansing the dead, straightening them, placing them in positions we recognize.

These things happen quickly; you blink and it's over. A second of inattention and all you can do is get everybody focused to pick up the pieces.

After we would get the wounded to their golden hours, people would straighten the dead. Line them up, retrieve pieces of them and place the parts under sheets to make it look like they were whole. They try to put children next to their parents, husbands near their wives. Anything to make it seem less random while the dead waited to be taken away. As if they waited for anything. As if they had anything left to wait for while we waited, tasting the copper dirt, until we could go on to the next moment, then the next, then the next, imagining what it would be like to be them.

The trick is, teaching them to put their minds in another space during those moments. You deal with it matter-of-factly, just another moment and these things around, supine, limp, straightened out, these are not the ones you knew. These are only the leftovers. This is the shell of a once living being. Now it does not live. They were confounded and blundered into becoming prey. There is no blaming it for its death.

And who do you find to blame? Where are the ones at fault? They believe, those who come with the bomb strapped to their chests or driving that car or taping that cell phone to the shell. They see only a feral animal, vicious, diseased, big and threatening. They see evil. They see the devil in it, begging for extermination.

Blame seems pointless.

Here's how I learned about waterboards.

Thirty-some years ago, I'd heard about it. Everybody knew about it. They knew somebody would get the waterboard. The course had an acronym, from the words Survival, Evasion, the good part, Resistance. I suppose it didn't look right with the contraction "SER," so I figure they added another "E" to make it "SERE." But nobody ever Escapes. All that "E" for Escape stuff was just as uncatchable as Billy's hummingbirds.

As training goes, it was good. I admit it. You're out of your element. The rules go away. The other guys who can't escape stand in ranks with make-believe guards screaming and pushing on them. What you do, you try to imagine what it would really be like to be in a POW camp—knowing no one will come. You toughen up by making believe these guards will, in the end, make you prey.

The instructors chose an officer. They put the officer up for everyone to watch. They were careful, a doctor standing by, a shrink. At first you try to hold your breath, but the sheet over your face seems to tighten up, mashing in your nose, and your arms and legs are caught immobile, so all you can do is try not to move, because if you do, you might slip away from being able to actually take in a breath. Then you gag. And you can't keep control anymore. You lose your wits. You thrash. You scream, puke and aspirate water. They lift the board up at the feet with your head down so they can control it. The doctor and the shrink keep their eye on you to make sure it doesn't get out of hand. Someone, just when I lost hope, dug me out.

They tell you there's no shame in all that. They tell you it's training. There's no blame in it. The rule for captivity is survival with honor.

I don't know what anyone else got out of it. Nobody wanted to talk to me about it. Ever. And I didn't talk to anyone who'd watched. What I learned?

Never be the prey.

What happened to Billy? He was out of his element. When we got him at the shelter, they told us he'd grown up in an apartment, never went out, so when we took him in, he stepped up. He got our garden where he could pee on the plants, the lawn where he could roll around in the sun picking up fleas and the porch where the hummingbirds came down whenever they were bored to bitch him out. He was happy, but clueless. Always bewildered and dumb.

Caroline said, "So we blame the cat?"

But the cat can't be blamed either. He was an accident waiting to happen. Didn't know about hummingbirds, didn't know about poodles.

The guy they put up on the board was out of his element. He didn't know about these people who had him. He didn't know what was going to happen. What they told me, they found him at the scene. He wouldn't talk. So they were only going to give him a little tooth and see what happened. So I said okay. You can't cup them in your hands every minute. You must let them do.

The way we put it, we were looking for reason, some hysterical twitch of truth. But watching the film, it was just prey at that moment before passing from life. It was a creature, in between, not knowing whether or not he should try to sit up.

And I could see it was us, we who'd learned the trick of feeling the worm twitch in our fingers, but viewing it as inconsequential.

Caroline is as Catholic as a human being can be; when she looks in the mirror she sees a Catholic girl then and Catholic woman now and a Catholic eternity. And I am Catholic with her.

I don't ask her to change. I don't blame her. I am not worthy to receive you, but only say the word and I shall be healed, I pray.

I pray the rosary, take a lap around the beads daily. I say "Hail Mary, full of grace." I say, "Pray for us sinners now and at the hour of our death, Amen." When Caroline puts her arm around me, I feel comforted. I think it's possible I have erred. It's possible I am forgiven.

But at night they come with the wet sheet and I balance this cardboard tube over my mouth. If I move, it may fall away. I grip back my panic, knowing that sooner or later I will not be able to keep it inside; it will spill out. No saving spade will slice down to end it. No careful arm over my shoulder will pull me closer ever again.

Caroline fixes blame. It's in her nature. She is not to blame. She has found her absolution; she knows who is to blame. They are. Those others. I don't tell her everything.

Some things, I don't trust her to know.

But someday, maybe, someone will show up to ask. Someone will come with a picture, and I'll say I guess I had seen that. I'll say there might have been a little tussle. They'll have questions about reason and disorder, acts of commission and omission. There will be blame. I do not believe there will be a comforting arm around my shoulder.

Or, perhaps, no one will come. Perhaps there will be no questions, no search for blame, no search for any sort of truth, and it will go on as it is. Me basking, pretending there's solace, ignoring those confounding birds.

Either way—this is the point—I cannot bring myself to sit up, not knowing how deep it is above me. So I wait, out of my element, at that in-between moment with no golden hour.

And no one will say the word.

And I will not be healed. This I know.

Ever.

Kathleen McGookey/Grief's Pretty Prize

What is the difference between lament and complaint?
Today I am all mouth, unsatisfied.

The dictionary won't say how to erase the ache.
What have I filled by the end of the day? Glasses

of water, bushels of peaches. Given a recipe, everyone
expects clarity, expects of the three wishes, one will be

for the perfect pie crust. Which vanishes, as it should,
into a family's mouths. They have gathered around a table.

I know I shouldn't say they are bathed in light. But look—a whole
family, not one member gone. The mouth in the sky

or the earth or the garage has closed, temporarily
full. Grief has not begun with them. But I am

grief's pretty prize. Someday I will tell you my story:
imagine me in the hospital's hallways, lit by green exit signs,

pushing the baby's stroller longer than you'd think I could,
in that clean bright light, away from someone I love.

Kathleen McGookey/Sorrow Came

Because she was called. Like the minister, like the undertaker, she speaks softly. When no one else will, she mentions my parents. How my mother loved butterscotch. How my father loved socket sets.

Now I am used to her. She spends all day looking at the back of my head. If I turn, she turns too.

When I learn everything about her, will she go?

Michael Boccardo/The Poem Disguised as an Ex-Lover

You know the kind: she appears on your doorstep
three weekends out of the month, spinning
the same tired simile—poor as a sock deprived of a foot.
But you take her in and sacrifice sleep until she creates
a story credible enough to justify the luggage bulging
beneath your eyes. She camps on the sofa until midnight,
then sails through the house in a cloak of musk,
her knuckles and neckline adorned like a chandelier,
the town tease stapled in red silk.
She doesn't call, not once, but you wait, obedient, till four
in the morning, every nail worried down to a bloody quarter moon,
each muscle double corded, joints taut as rubber bands.
When the familiar crack of stilettos stumbles past the threshold
you soak into the carpet's green fabric with something like relief,
then help her into bed the way you've been trained.
It doesn't matter if her neck wears a scarf of cheap cologne
you'd never own or her whiskey laden lips unlock a name
heard in the dim flutter of smoky clubs, a name that unzips her dress
and invents new verbs for the ivory scroll of her body.
All you want is a flawless night of sleep, to stop sipping stale coffee
from the cesspool of grimy mugs abandoned in the kitchen sink,
to forget about ever understanding the oblivion billowing
across her face when you demand enough is enough.
But the moment she fades through the door's blank page,
it will always be the same story, your arm lifting,
poised, as if waiting for inspiration to return,
like the slanted spine of an uncapped pen.

Janice Lierz/Making Hats

I have never made a hat—
not with glass beads or any
sequins and ribbons.

At Macy's my five sisters and I try
them on, making faces in the mirror—pleased with how we look—
not pleased with how we look.

"You look like Mom," we say
for the ultimate insult.
I slip into the quiet

dressing room with three-way
mirrors and a cushioned bench
in a raspberry beret—

I am exotic and foreign—
something I would never buy.
The saleslady comes in,

"It's not for you, dear," she says,
and I blink and slip it from my head.
There is no doubt

others have made hats
with glass beads and ribbons—
sequins that catch light.

But the nearest I have ever come
to making hats
was making myself

underneath one.

Janice Lierz/The Tree of Us

I bought you a tree for our anniversary,
for you to stir life from the dirt,

its exquisite reach a picture
book of green and yellow
in autumn,
just like I remember your hair.

The woman at the checkout
seemed embarrassed to tell me
there were no guarantees here
for a Japanese maple.

Too many were lost
in the late frost
last spring.
Remove the clay, she said.

Don't be afraid to dirty your hands.
Turn topsoil with minerals,
but the secret to its brilliance
would be cow manure.

And I thought—
yes, this is marriage.

Carla Panciera/Alone in the Tiverton House

The dog, drowsy from yesterday's anesthesia, naps.
The cancer, for now, is gone.

Dennis has taken the girls to the playground,
sun off the monkey bars, their palms wrung with cold.

February, no boats on the river, the clock frozen.

Hours ago, one hundred seven geese floated by. A hawk
swung low, his shadow undulating over the smooth-stoned beach.

Nothing moves now but river and sun lowering itself to water.

If a door closes on the opposite shore,
someone home at the end of a day, it does so without my notice.

There were days everyone else returned to someone.
But here again is the life I had, an afternoon of my own noises.

What's different? The river, this room,
where a lily's leaf extends a fraction of an inch.

I follow a lone gull after a late crab as if the bird is proof.
Of what? That one life is simpler than any other?

Maybe just that relative silence exists and in it I sit,
all my love accounted for.

In the time the sun takes to touch river, it is possible to need nothing.

Austin Tremblay/The Town I Happened to Be in Was Home

That's what I have to think,
walking over the uneven stones
of downtown, staring at the dead
buildings, just bigger stones, stationary
ghosts. The mind is happily haunted
by wet streets, the sound
of water, the tightness of gravel,
but the body, salt in each eye,
will float on anything larger
than itself without worry.

It's the reason I leave
porches, praise stray dogs, drink
in the wrong bars until I can't relearn
my way around. I don't know
how to be here on purpose.

On Front St., a vagrant moans,
begging even for the words
to beg with. I hear him all the way
down Market, until I get to the river,
where there is nothing but the green
and black of camouflage bathing
the wreckage I think is me.
There is no sound here, no lover
I can be true to. Only the water reflecting
nothing, slapping concrete, the dock
cuffing any current, both of them
saying, "Be still."

It's the reason I have to stay
in a hotel, why I moan too
for a different language than this one.
Even this poem I couldn't write

with my own pen. I naturally picked
up the complimentary one,
which no one takes with them
when they leave what they know
is not home.

Nancy Aldrich/**Rooms above the Street**

The sparrows are gone always wings
angled away and up like leaves caught
windward unpredictable by my
calculation.

Once lying in bed I thought the birds
were leaves, the leaves falling up not
down were birds. I seem to have hours
of time for this.

The bones of my knees are
cold. It is possible to imagine that a year
from now I will not
be alive.

Whether or not I am of what my critical
daughter calls the dominant
culture, no one can know how solitary is my
count of the grackles. I have

forgotten how to write a letter. For
the life of me I could not string
stockings along a fireplace mantel but I can
see somebody

doing this. I can observe for days changes
in weather, will it snow? Sometimes
I walk in my trailing black wool coat remembering
another coat.

Kimberly K. Farrar/Talk

for Laura Dean, diagnosed with Autism, 1999

Start with the personal pronouns:
You, me, I.
Then take the verb To Be.
This is an aviary.

Perhaps I could teach you to sew
instead. We could string the alphabet
onto your shoelaces. A blurry whirl
of magnetic letters: blue, green, red.

Take mine.
I know how to wend
my way through the forsythia.
I know the beauty
of blather, wisp, mandible.

I don't need to talk.
Take my tongue, root and all.
Place it under your pillow
where the tooth fairy
might exchange our dilemma
for a shiny coin.
You'll awaken to say, "Momma, look
at my dime."

Brandon Krause/Windfall

Photography begs simple luck at best.
Astute and careful eyes sincerely see
Those palisades where oceans crawl to rest
And trade their tired wrath for destiny.
Some art escapes through objects no one sought,
This sweet Unknown with wealth so rarely seized,
I keep a stable hand to shake the thought,
My outcome will betray the prize's tease.
A thoughtful gaze to capture citadels,
The ancient forts that filled those starving stares
Of vagabonds and thieves from distant knolls;
My lens finds beauty even in despair.
Such warmth, this film so ripe with blossomed chance,
I wait to taste the windfall in these hands.

Jessica Treadway/Deprivation

The baby had been crying for nine hours. Since four o'clock in the morning, through all of Nina's beseeching and ministrations—re-diapering, trying to feed, shuffling around the house while rocking him up and down, sitting in front of the TV, holding him like a football, showing him every stuffed animal she could find, putting him down on his back, putting him down on his stomach, putting him in the baby swing, bathing him, and singing—he kept it up, not a rhythmic squall which would have worn him out eventually, but a continuous mewling she thought might go on forever. Curtis left for work at the usual time, around eight-thirty, after kissing both of them and wishing Nina luck. He told her he would call around lunchtime, but when one o'clock came and went without the phone ringing, she cursed him and turned on a soap opera. This was something she had told both herself and Curtis she wouldn't do—start watching daytime TV while she stayed home with the baby—but it was an emergency, she told herself. If Norton didn't stop crying, she didn't know what she would do.

The baby was named Norton after the character on *The Honeymooners*, Curtis's favorite show. In the five months since the birth, Nina had regretted, often, capitulating to this request. She had been thinking more along the lines of Kevin or Eric. But somehow Curtis had convinced her that people would think it was cool, and funny, to have a child named after the Art Carney character. There would be no other Nortons at school, he pointed out to Nina. Now she thought of this more as a reason to have nixed the idea. Her son would suffer—this she could already tell, when strangers asked and learned of the baby's name. They tried to cover it up, but Nina could tell they believed she had bad judgment. And she didn't, really—Curtis just got to her, one night while they were watching a rerun and Ed Norton was particularly kooky, and she thought that giving the name to their son would make him independent and original. So: Norton. Luckily, he wasn't old enough yet to know what a stupid name he had. For all he knew, he *was* a Kevin or an Eric.

On the soap opera, a serial killer was on the loose. Three citizens of Salem had already been murdered, the last one having been the wife of the pub owner and the mother of the city's police captain. The dead character's name was Caroline. That's a nice name, Nina thought. Why couldn't we have had a girl? But then Curtis would probably have talked her into *Trixie*. While she was watching the TV, Nina put Norton in his playpen and just let him cry. She turned the sound up and knew she was being a bad mother, but figured she would start dealing with it again at two o'clock.

Caroline was lying in her open casket in a tasteful white suit, with her family and friends around her. Every time someone came over to say good-bye, or to touch her hand, she just lay there, but when the character of Celeste was by the casket, Caroline came back to life. Celeste was psychic — she could always tell when something bad was going to happen, and she read Tarot cards. Her son-in-law had been the murderer's first victim.

But even though she was used to her own intuitions, Celeste was freaked out when she heard Caroline whisper to her from the coffin. Nothing *quite* so psychic had ever happened to her before.

From her silk pillow, the corpse of Caroline said to Celeste, "The killing is not over. I'm telling you, Celeste, because you understand these things."

In her shock, and making sure to whisper so none of the mourners noticed, Celeste asked, "Is *anyone* safe?"

The corpse shook her beautifully coiffed head and said, "Everyone in Salem is in danger. Please, Celeste, warn everyone. There is more evil on the way." Then, as somebody else came up to the casket, she returned to the still and silent dead person she was supposed to be. The credits rolled and the program was over. Nina cursed.

She called Curtis at work. He developed software for global positioning systems, and even though most of his work was in the office, they made him wear his hair in a ponytail, in case any clients ever dropped by.

"He's still crying," Nina said.

"How come?"

She imagined putting his ponytail down the waste disposal and flipping on the switch. It was an image that had come to her before. "I have no idea, Curtis. Do you think if I had any idea, I'd be calling you? Don't you remember him crying this morning?" But she knew he had slept through it. He had once slept through a Patriots game, *at* the stadium.

"Nina, babies cry." She could tell he wanted to get off the phone, which probably meant there was a supervisor nearby. But she wasn't about to let him.

"They don't cry for *ten hours straight*, Curtis. And if you're so blasé about it, why don't you come home and take care of him? I just need to get out of this house. I need to hear something besides this goddam sound."

"Nina," he said, in the patronizing voice that made her fantasize about cutting the ponytail off while he slept, "you know I can't come home right now. I'm out here earning a living. But why don't you call a babysitter? Pay her extra if he cries the whole time."

A babysitter. It hadn't occurred to her. She didn't know what her chances were, on short notice, but she said she would try.

She was lucky. She got Angela Civetti just as she walked in the door from school. "I need to run a few errands," Nina said. "It wouldn't be long." Angela said she could be right over. "Great!" Nina said, then thought she should tone it down so as not to make the teenager suspicious. "I really appreciate it, Angela. See you soon." Watch, she told herself, Norton'll stop screaming as soon as Angela gets here. Like when you take your car to the shop and it's stopped making the clunking noise.

But that didn't happen. When Angela arrived, the baby's cheeks were red and swollen from crying all day, and he was still at it. "He's been a little fussy," Nina said, "but maybe you can get him to sleep in the swing." That she had tried this strategy several times already, without success, she didn't tell the babysitter. "I should be back in an hour or so," she said, trying to gauge how long would be too unfair to ask of a sixteen-year-old without sufficient warning about what she was in for. "Oh, and help yourself to the cake on the counter. We had it for Curtis's birthday."

Too late, she remembered that Angela Civetti was the *bulimic* babysitter. Nina had had to call the plumber once when she clogged up the toilet with thrown-up food. But she couldn't take the offer back now.

She could hear Norton's crying until she was at the end of the driveway. It had snowed fourteen inches during the weekend and Nina hadn't been out to drive since, so she had to adjust and pay attention to the slippery road. She went to Walgreens and wandered the aisles, picking out things she would need sooner or later: mouthwash (soon); a birthday card for her mother (the end of the month); a can of formula; and a set of colored plastic keys for Norton, as if that might be the magic thing he needed, what he'd been crying for all along.

When she returned home she found not Angela but Curtis, bouncing a screeching Norton on his knee. "What are you doing here?" Nina said. "It's not even four."

"I told them I had an emergency at home," he said. He was still wearing his work clothes, brown corduroys, a yellow button-down and a tie with tumbling circus bears. "After you called I felt crummy for being a jerk." He turned to look at her for the first time since she'd come in and collapsed, still in her coat, on the couch. "Hey, what happened to my cake? I was looking forward to a piece."

"Oh, God." Nina went into the kitchen and saw the empty cake plate soaking in the sink. She made a note to herself to look up the plumber's number as soon as Norton stopped crying—if he ever did.

"Do you think we should call the doctor?" Curtis laid Norton on his back and twisted off his tie.

"Wait a minute. Just let me try something." Nina reached into the Walgreens bag and pulled out the plastic keys. She shook them in front of her son's face, but it only made him cry harder.

"Hey, I like those," Curtis said. "I think I had one of them when I was a kid."

"Well, the doctor's a good idea," Nina said, going to the phone. "At least the timing's good—they have call-in from four to four-thirty."

The nurse was so sympathetic it made Nina want to cry. "He'll be fine, honey," she told Nina, after determining that Norton's temperature had been taken and was normal. "It's probably colic. I don't usually recommend this, but if he's really been crying for that long, I'd give him some Benadryl. It should put him right out. He needs to sleep, if he's been awake this long."

"Thank you so much," Nina said. She wanted to stay on the line with this calm and comforting woman, but she knew other people needed to get through. She went into the bathroom and got the Benadryl, and with Curtis stroking Norton's forehead, she squeezed an eye-dropper full of the pink medicine into her son's mouth. "That should do it," she said, and sure enough, within fifteen minutes the baby was asleep, and Curtis and Nina called out for a pizza.

They had four hours until Norton woke up again. They were lying on the two couches in the living room, both facing the TV. Curtis had tuned in to *Cops*, and Nina found herself drifting to the sounds of sirens and the voices of police officers as they pulled people over or chased them through yards. Then it was a baby crying and she jerked awake, having to catch her breath. "Shit!" she said, afraid of something she couldn't remember.

Curtis had already gotten up and gone into Norton's room. The baby was squalling on his back, his fists clenched and his face red, and Nina followed Curtis around the room as he changed the diaper and put on fresh clothing. "He has to eat," she said, and they had another ten minutes of quiet while Norton sucked down the contents of a full bottle. Then he began again. Nina sat in a chair and stared at the floor. She pressed her hands against her eyes until she saw explosions.

"I'll take him out," Curtis said.

"In this weather?"

"Well, I'll have the heat on. You know how the car calms him down." He began pulling on his own jacket and boots while Nina dressed the baby and wrapped him in his alphabet quilt for good measure. "I'll drive till he falls asleep. Don't wait up," he said grimly.

With the baby gone it took a full half hour to get the sound of his screaming out of her head. She turned off the TV and picked up her book, which she had chosen from the library shelves because it was skinny, and the only way she could read anything, these days, was in short shifts. *The Stranger.* She opened it to the first page. *"Maman died today."* The words caused her eyes to swell with hot tears, not because of her own mother, who was alive and well and serving her fellow mankind as an Emergency Medical Technician in Mamaroneck, but because she herself was a mother now, and someday her son might read these same words and feel a burst of tenderness toward her, of the kind she had felt toward him since shortly after she knew he was growing inside her. Then she grew sad thinking of the pain Norton would suffer when she died, then sadder still when she realized that *he* would die, this fresh baby becoming an old man, if he was lucky; she couldn't bear the idea of him leaving the world she had so recently witnessed him enter, so she shook the thoughts away and focused on the story. Meursault, the main character, was at the beach in Algiers, and the sun was so hot it made his eyebrows drip, and cymbals of sunlight crashed upon his forehead. He couldn't tell whether the Arab man was coming at him with a knife. *"The sun was the same as it had been the day I'd buried Maman, and like then, my forehead especially was hurting me, all the veins in it throbbing under the skin. It was this burning, which I couldn't stand anymore, that made me move forward."* When she had finished reading about the murder she put the book aside and looked at the clock; Curtis and the baby had been gone for nearly two hours. She was just standing up, not knowing where her next step would take her, when she heard the car in the driveway and they were home.

He was still crying. "Did he sleep at all?" she asked Curtis, whose hair was hanging loose down to his shoulders—she could never get him to wear a hat.

He shook his head. "I drove all the way to Worcester," he told her almost in a whisper, as if it were his own voice on the verge of giving out. "I couldn't stand it anymore. Did *you* sleep?"

"No. I couldn't. I'm reading this weird book." They both looked at Norton, still bundled in his carrier in the middle of the kitchen floor, his mouth open so wide they could see his tonsils throbbing in his throat.

"You go to bed," she told Curtis. "It's my turn."

"Do you think the hospital, if he doesn't stop soon?"

She considered. "The nurse said it was just colic. I've read about it, they cry for no reason. He has to get tired soon. Doesn't he?"

Curtis said he didn't know and lifted his feet to let his boots fall off in thuds. He kissed in the direction of Nina and padded down the hall to the bedroom, where he shut the door.

She unwrapped her son and took him back into the living room with her. She tried the swing and the TV. She tried singing, and offered him more formula. Every attempt seemed to make him cry harder, though she knew that at a certain point—which he had reached long ago—this was impossible.

She propped him against a cushion of the couch. She thought she could feel every nerve in her body, trembling. Norton watched her as he wailed, but he could have no idea what it meant to see his mother pick up another cushion and, breathing aloud, draw it close to his heaving face. She held it softly over his mouth and nose, just for a moment, long enough to muffle the crimson shriek. Then she took the pillow away, pitched it across the room, picked him up and began to rock.

It didn't help. He kept on crying.

In the morning, Curtis came out still wearing his T-shirt and boxers. "I'm staying home today," he told Nina.

"Oh, God, thank you."

"It's not for you. I feel lousy." They had to shout at one another over the sound of their son. He went to the kitchen to make coffee.

"Lousy as in sick?" She left Norton on his back on the living room floor, and came toward her husband.

"No. Lousy as in no sleep." He leaned against the counter with both hands, looking out the window. "I'll go out with the snowblower today, as long as I'm home."

"Oh! Maybe you could take him out in the backpack. He loves it with the lawnmower, maybe the snowblower would work the same."

Curtis looked at her with what she would have interpreted as hatred, if she didn't know better. "If you think so," he said without enthusiasm. "But won't he be cold?"

"I'll bundle him up again." Norton's crying had gone way beyond giving her a headache, to the point that she thought she might vomit. She began packing the baby into his snowsuit while Curtis went to get dressed.

It was cold outside, though the sun shone against the snow. Nina jiggled Norton on her hip while Curtis adjusted the backpack straps, and then she lowered the baby in. Curtis winced as his son's screams hit the back of his head. He went to the garage, pushed the snowblower out, and turned it on. In the house, Nina nearly wept from the relief of hearing a different noise.

From the living room window, she watched as they came into view, and she could feel her jaw actually drop as she saw that Norton had not only stopped crying, but also was smiling and slapping at the air with his mittens. Tears and snot still streaked his face, but he was happy.

She rapped on the window and Curtis looked up. She pointed behind him and he craned to see his son, then turned back to her and gave the thumbs-up. She went to bed and tried to sleep, but her heart was racing, so she got up again and opened her book.

The judge was asking Meursault what had caused him to kill the Arab man at the beach. Meursault thought for a moment, and then he replied that he had shot the man because of the sun. Everybody in the courtroom laughed, but Nina understood perfectly.

It took Curtis an hour to clear their driveway and the sidewalk in front of the house. When he turned the snowblower off and came in for lunch, Norton started crying again. "Dammit," he said to Nina, who had finished the book and was folding baby socks on the sofa. "I was afraid of this."

"Maybe you'll have to blow out the Durfees, too," she suggested. She thought she was joking, but Curtis blew on his soup and took a glum swallow.

"Maybe I will."

After lunch he put on his wet clothes and took the baby on his back again, and Norton cheered right up. Nina checked to make sure they were out of sight, in the neighbors' driveway, before she turned on the TV. The killer was back at it in Salem, and she watched the whole hour with the drone of the snowblower safely in the distance. At two o'clock she turned off the TV. The theme song from *Cops* was running through her head, and she found herself whispering the words. "'Bad boys, bad boys, whatcha gonna do? Whatcha gonna do when they come for you?'" Then she laughed at herself and loaded the dishwasher.

It was close to four o'clock when her boys came back. Curtis had cleared two more driveways and part of the cul-de-sac. Sure enough, as soon as he'd turned off the snowblower, Norton took up his noise again. This time Nina fed him two droppers of Benadryl, and within ten minutes he had fallen asleep.

Curtis and Nina sat next to each other on the couch, both slumped and exhausted. Curtis said, "Maybe I shouldn't tell you this, but while I was out there I had an image of burying him in the snow, if he didn't stop crying. I know that sounds terrible."

"It does." Nina spoke quietly. She was tracing the pattern of the pillow with her finger.

"But it made me see how these things happen. I feel like I understand, now, how people can abuse their kids." Curtis put his feet up on the table and went to wrap his arm around her, but she leaned away. It was a barely noticeable movement, but they both felt it.

"What's the matter?" He flipped a tendril of his hair back over his shoulder, to get it out of their way. "You mean *you* never thought of it before, with all this crying?"

"Of course not. What kind of a mother would I be?" But she didn't want him to answer her. Instead—because she didn't know what it would mean if she stayed away—she let herself move back toward him, forcing herself to snuggle into his side.

"A normal one, I think," Curtis said, but she was already falling asleep to a dream of a glittering Algerian beach, an Arab with a knife, the sun beating down to blind her as she lifted the pistol and, with little thought about what the Arab might have done to deserve it, fired.

Patricia Clark/The Amputee Dance

Some days it's better not to stop, to bend over with the shears
and cut what troubles you off. If it's your hand,
or your foot, still cut. You can learn an amputee dance.

Some days it's better not to stay or wonder. Grab the key
and start the car, let it pull you to the highway,
don't let yourself look up. That shadow's the hawk.

At the post office, some days it's better not to hear—
on every side a complaint, a lament, a cry. The eyes
of the clerk show a faint alarm, mouth clamps shut.

Some days it's better to strike out and swim, whether in air
or river water, Lake Michigan, puddle water, ditch or creek.
Current's better than still, cooler than hot to the touch.

It's looser some days to start a fire—permitted or not—
and light up bundles of your papers, then clothes,
not an exit so much as transformation, or molt.

Isn't it better sometimes to give in to wet, to let be,
to the shoulders hunched, the face in rags, the hand
limp, the legs rubbery and not able to walk,

to say or write nothing, to eat silence for nourishment,
to refuse the meal, requested or not, to close the pores,
the ears, all the pleasure orifices, all the pain.

Some days it's better at the altar of the rose, the grave
of the ant, the bed of mulch where a fungus grows,
spreading like an oatmeal-colored spill. Why can't you stop

noticing? Some days what's better is a piano key struck
over and over, then cajoled into melody, trilled into song,
so what if the singer is dead, for a while she had this voice.

Patricia Clark/Psalm to the Toad

Look where he sits, sheltered by hosta and toad house.
A terra cotta curve for a roof, his color is the earth.
He waits like mud. He knows that lunch will wing along.

What must the sprinkler sound like to him at night?
The most natural of rains, it cools his world.
Hopping out in the early hours, he makes a proverb:
Behold the toad—slow to move but hidden in place.

He sits on his haunches, the posture of thought.
His throat beats a faint pulse under leathery skin,
the only sign of his life. Even the cat's fooled.

His eyes, rimmed by a faint gold, barely blink.
How can toad take up arms against his enemies?
Old wise one, unlovely with your dark warty skin,
you show by patience that claws can be stymied.

When the mower comes, lie low as a rock.
When the dog sniffs, simply outlast him.
When someone lifts your roof, find home under the pine.

You who relish the flagstone, the mulch, the curving frond
of Solomon's seal, its white berries globes to light
your world, there's no forgetting how your ancestor struggled here
after the snake's fang. I vow to protect you, as I can.

Brian Johnson/Intent

I mean to streamline myself. To remove the stacked newspapers, the rows of unworn shirts, the thumbed novels—and stand up, a man in a field.

I mean to be simple, but the night—the fresh air—it troubles me. No one is so disengaged. Every sensation requires a word, a step away.

I mean to be predictable, like the one driving slowly on the familiar street, and the one heading slowly to the familiar house.

I mean to leave behind my dirty world and all its dirty faces. I mean to come to the door, triumphant, beaten into love.

Brian Johnson/The World to Come

No street without a theater. No building without a bird. Dogs in the sun. People crying, *we're here, we're here.* No parks with gates. No museums. More footpaths than roads. More holidays without names. No building with a name. People crying here and there and nowhere, *we made it, we made it.* No directions except the scribbled ones. No passes except for the sun. No monuments with dates. No gilded men, no fallen women. People sitting in the rushes, on branches, on sand, running in and out of passages, shouting *we're home, we're home.*

Helen Wickes/Daedalus

I go on and what else is a maker to do. I mourn, I go on.

My handiwork melted and disfigured before my eyes, beyond all
beauty and function as observed in the hummingbird, the vulture,

but he was my spawn, my foal, my own sweet fool
whom I launched, and he failed us both, he did.

For everything I make, something's unmade.

Hurled west—*old artificer*—I unfurled my fingertips which ached
for the next thing of wonder fated for me to set loose,

as with my hands I made these—air lifters, sky sifters—pummeled
and pinched the wax, articulated each sinew, doomed as I am

to survive through my own sheer brilliance. Not my fault
he was dumb as a bag of hammers, but mine he was, and *it was*

my day. I'm uncontainable as air,
while he was of the more perishable earth. Of wren,

sparrow, hawk—the many nasty dead things I learned from—the owl
as well as the starling. I taught him to soar, to use the wind shift,
to float, dip, slice through clouds, but he screwed it up

and it wasn't my fault, now, was it.

A father I was, but a maker too. And since these are the world's
perfect wings, I won't take flight with others, not ever.

And so we ascended, and he wasn't all that dumb, just heedless,
and I buried him, I mourned, I went on.

I fixed row upon row of feathers, precisely, as I saw
the journey, in my mind's eye, already existing, and it telling me
to follow. Fierce thing the mind,

there were fields of gold, and we were meant to see them.
Everything made, as I've said, it gets unmade.

We waved to fishermen, to shepherds, who must have thought
we were gods, headed as we were to the fields of barley.

Helen Wickes/In Praise of Yellow

In sunlight through grains of sand and shell, or any
small joy, the coherence of egg yolk, the vagueness
of air, the bells that ring only at midday, tawny light
on the hillside, a taxicab idling at night in the rain,
moonlight in a puddle, pee in the snow, down the road,
double lines propelling your flight in a smoldering rage,
turmeric and cumin, what's sallow and fearful, a secret
the topaz tells, the thread that draws forth your soul, as
played in C major on a flute, scent of saffron, and how he
buttered his corn, how she cupped the flames, the palomino's
crest, the boy's amber hair, what's burning or glowing, yes,
and the moldering, the golden as well, the sulfurs from hell,
from nowhere a yell of surprise, bright splash of lemon
on your tongue, that yellow room you can't step foot in
again, its curtains and walls, in memory where you dwell,
out the window, a field of mustard, the throat of a finch.

Curtis Luckey/Shoes

The closet sneaks open,
with a single pair of shoes.
You know the ones, black,
that you only get to wear once.

You step into the dark, past a door
that would close behind you, if it were
still there when you turned around.
Then you put on the shoes.

They're a Perfect Fit.

You step deeper, into dark,
Deeper, into warmth,
Deeper—until,

Suddenly, you see a light,
a light you walk to, but then you stop.
It shines damp, it shines cold, creeping
your flesh, like icy worms.

So you turn around, or at least
you try.
But the shoes
walk deeper into light,
Deeper into cold.
Deeper—until. . .
Now you're in the light,
freezing. Wet. Gone.
All but the shoes.
They run back to the closet,

for the next, Perfect Fit.

Nancy Botkin/The Next Infinity

1.

All that talk about Jesus
pointing to God made us lighter.
Or was it the horizon in every direction
after we left church
and caravanned to the little country cemetery?
Maybe it was seeing the equipment
farmers use to disc the earth.

At first the rain fell like feathers.

That was one infinity,

and we had to step over its broken glass.

2.

Pompeii buried in a violent storm of ash.
We walk over the rubble
and pause to look at the frescoes
above the doors in the brothel.
Doors
lead to other doors,
and stark light
cuts a sharp angle across a stone wall.

We hold that infinity close.

We play it from the infield.

3.

Rise out of the anesthesia.
No clarity around the ears, just buzzing.
Just babbling

and involuntary tears.
It's cold, so cold.

Doctor, how often do we change the gauze?

Smear the stars across the face of that infinity

and come up for air.

4.

For anyone who's ever felt starved,
or brittle,
or that the day has no curve to it,
no vacancy,
embrace infinity's echo, like shallow
breath,
or darkness in the pit of forever.

5.

Stick a bookmark in this infinity

and come back to it later.

The dark red claw of passion leaves its mark.

Beautiful terror of a radiant half moon.
Beautiful emptiness of a silent piano.

Beautiful flapping at the ears
when the tongue touches
the innumerable stars winking
along the untamed ocean of flesh.

Impossible to avoid all the broken glass
hidden in the sand.

Carry on dancing.
Carry on fumbling in the dark.

Light candles, yes, but we need
something more than that, don't we?

Who can resist singing just one note
when the lightening
is so white,
so gold,
so white gold?

6.

An autopsy of infinity would uncover the barest, most
stripped down field.

7.

What defines your next to nothing?

The prayer, the hymn, or the ashes in the box?

Maybe the wind that streams over the tilled field.

Just a little anesthesia, please.
Undress the story, and place a star
over each unstressed syllable.

The next infinity will burn out like a super nova.
Its buzz will be light and distant.

Beneath the quiet, earth.

Beneath the shut eyes
a kind of darkness
that sparks
another darkness,
and that darkness
is infinite.

Nancy Botkin/The House is Quiet

My dreams fit nicely
into high-ceilinged rooms,
white as the nurses' uniforms

of long ago.

My father thought he could address
all problems with violence.
(Hence my face pressed into corners

where I had missed the dirt.)

There's something calming
about a hardwood floor's color
and sheen. There's something calming

about walking across it in stilettos.

Even better when the room is empty.
There's a faint echo, and I am aware
someone's watching me.

Flowers too can't be without praise.

Transported inside,
they're surrounded by artifice—track lighting,
a still life, and the wild

popping of central heat.

Cully Pappas/Sun Song

What muse, or was it jester, plotted this—
To shoot an arrow tipped with darkest night,
So swift its course that even loving kiss
Was blinded by the danger of its flight?
Who thought to steal the sacred bonds and why
Defile the joy of love most dearly held?
Such evil spirits swirling in the sky
Shall surely spin relentlessly unquelled.
The radiance of life that warmed my days,
Now stolen by a prankster on the run.
A story sung by minstrels as they play—
These traitors hide in shadows dark and deep,
And plunder purest pleasures while we sleep.

Randall Brown/How You Write a Story

Find someone. Give him a name. Call him Spenser, after your grandfather, whose house you could run to as if it were "base" and someone else was "it." Make Spenser ten years old. Put him on Meadow Lane, where the houses sit back against a creek, and on the opposite side, woods grow wild. Make the trees birch, because Robert Frost wrote about birches and boys and turned white like grandfathers.

The boy runs the way little boys run, unafraid of bursting hearts or empty breaths. He runs like the characters in dreams, pursued by darkness more than something substantial. Give the boy curls, his mother's dimple, his father's olive Greek skin. Picture an infant Greek god, lithe. Give him something real to run from, put it in his hand. Make it a love note to his mother, from a neighbor, or his dad's best friend, or maybe both.

Obstacles should appear in his way and make it difficult to reach his grandfather, make the arrival at the dead end and his grandfather's house hard earned. But nothing appears for the boy, just pavement, the bent birches. Give him a season. Fall. And now leaves crunch under him and oranges and yellows rush by as if the world ran on and on and he stood still. He could trip, but Spenser doesn't even stumble. Remember he's nimble. A tiny Greek god.

Take a breath. Consider for a moment what you are afraid to face, why Spenser must make imagined runs with imagined notes through imagined seasons to an imagined dead end. Think about the dark something you'd have to face if you stopped and turned around. Let the moment pass and turn back to Spenser, ten years old, and remember the fear only children feel, how all-encompassing it is, connected to the absence of things.

The note flutters in his hand. It sounds like a football card—Franco Harris!—in the spokes of the purple Schwinn.

The real creeps in. The card was yours, not Spenser's. Same with that bike. Same with the mother you loved so terribly and the father you loved a little bit less.

Face it. That's how you write a story.

Spenser gets there, bent like imagined birches. He's there, running to his grandfather, out of love and breath. He's not a Greek god. He's a little boy trembling with the fear of the world turning endlessly black.

The note says, "Meet me at the tennis courts. Score Love/Zero."

Spenser's grandfather finds his grandson bent and huffing and glistening.

Spenser holds up the note and his grandfather, white like Frost, reads it over his glasses. Spenser thinks of Santa, reading a list. His grandfather has twinkling eyes and a red-tipped nose.

"Oh," his grandfather says.

Again, a stillness. In that pause, the tiniest of epiphanies. Spenser isn't you. He's your son. And the grandfather is you. And the note the son holds in his hand is really this story. Score: Love/Zero.

"I'm done with love," Spenser tells his grandfather. He sounds too old in saying this. A ten-year-old would never say that. But this one does.

"Because of this?" The grandfather holds the note by the corner, as if it were a tissue full of snot.

"Don't say it's stupid. Because it isn't."

"To be done with love because of a note."

Your son interrupts you. He stands next to you at the computer and wonders what you are writing about this time.

Here's the important part. Convince yourself that the world is what it is only because of what you believe it to be. Believe in Spenser's world. Disbelieve that there was a note, a bike, house, a card, woods, grandfather, and Meadow Lane.

Your son reads the story slowly. He taps your shoulder and you scroll. You ask him, "What would you do, if you were that boy, holding that note?"

"It's just a story?" he asks.

"There's no note for you to find."

He touches the screen. The cursor blinks.

"Rip it up," he says.

The grandfather tears the note in half.

"Why?" you ask him.

"Then there isn't a note."

Explain that characters must find endings very hard to do. And that ripping the note changes nothing. It's too easy, too pat.

"Well, what would you do?" he asks.

I'd begin writing my own notes. I'd type them in the sleeping house and hide them like Easter eggs. In pockets. Purses. Wallets. The bottom of cereal boxes. Hundreds of them. Thousands of them, until they spilled out of the windows as from a burst pipe.

He's my son. My story. His name is Seth. You know what he does?

He says, "Oh, Dad. There was a note, wasn't there?"

Spenser can't stop crying. He wants to unfind the note, but the note cannot be unfound. He cries because the crime of his childhood will become the finding of that note. His grandfather won't let him leave. Not to that house. Not to that mother.

My son wraps me up. He says, "Poor Spenser."

Realize you don't know how to write a story.

Jill Gerard/Before Anyone Really Knew

Say it's autumn leaves, wind-mussed
yellow over red, slightly damp

geese flying, fluid and steady
one always emerging to replace the spent

a spring in late October, still burbling water
from some deep and secret well.

Or snow falling, muffling everything
before anyone really knew it had started—sudden then still

voices rising on a cold night, finding harmony
one note held, sharp and clear

fire crackling, wood snapping smoke
in waves across the sky.

Or crocus pushing up, impossibly bright
breaking the gray of late winter

wonder of bird song, quick trilling
coming from everywhere all at once

a dropped pebble that in its settling
sets the whole pond in motion.

Or a summer storm
clouds etched purple, full, waiting to let go

a hayfield heavy with seed, waving
stalks whispering softly one to the other their secret song

light entering the loft, warming dust
until it dances, rising and rising in just such a way.

Say it's a body, arcing up toward you
each muscle singing out its joy.

Jill Gerard/Night Walking

It is almost midnight
and the cadaver has disappeared.
He was sprawled across the chaise longue,
clutching a glass of Scotch.
The glass was sweaty, and he had complained of it.
He was hungry. Now here I am—
brie and crackers, raspberries and cream,
napkins, and he is gone.
So like a man.

Mushrooms dot the path through the woods,
like crumbs that he might have followed
down the hill, over the small crest,
and finally to the lake shore
where the water glows,
phosphorescence moving like magic.
Still no sign of him: not at the dock,
not in the boathouse, not ambling
along the small stretch of beach.

Only the frogs sing.
I decide to wait, dip my feet in black water,
moonlight brushing the whole world
into a silver-gelatin print,
just like the one I saw in the museum.

Finally, his step trembles the dock.
He is beside me, a few leaves stuck to the back of his shirt.
I was lying in the woods, smelling the damp earth, he confides.
I imagine the grave will be that way, the smell of damp earth,
the earthy taste of Scotch. I think that might be almost perfect.
He slips his hand into mine and we sit there
watching light play over water,
the woods creaking so slightly behind us.

Schubert Moore/Time to Die

This is when it hits the fan, old fool.
This is the last of the Mohicans, the acid test, the last brass tack.
This is the omega, the hard place, forever short a number of days.
You're out of water at the final bridge.
This is the bitter without the sweet.

It's time to shut up,
to ignore your blessings and count your chickens.
It's time to unhitch your wagon and open your hatch,
release the day and cast your pearls.
It's time to open your hand and loose the bird,
to pull the stitch, give up the ship.
It's time to switch from apples to bread.

The eggs are broken.
You ate your cake and another man's meat.
The dog's day is done and the cat is skinned.
The snow has melted. The tide won't wait.
It's pouring. It's too late to mend.
You know the enemy, but your iron's gone cold.
Sometimes there's just smoke.

Drop your rosebuds.
Ask the piper to pick a tune.
Turnabout and tango alone.
Go home.
Weep.
Lie down in the square hole.
Say die.

Schubert Moore/Cleanliness

Who said cleanliness is next to godliness?
I don't want a serene deity, white with purity,
antiseptic, who takes a cleanroom approach
to winnowing the wheat from the chaff.
Give me a jumble god,
a muddle of concoction,
frazzled with how complicated
the creation has become,
a little smudged around the edges,
more like myself.
I could believe in a god like that.

A clean creation? No unexpected stuff?
Then no penicillin,
bubblegum,
you.

Sometimes you get what you need,
a god who says
you're on your own
and washes his hands.

Jacqueline Tchakalian/Mead

I want a man to pull
milk from my breasts;
know taste, fragrance
honeyed intoxication

lock his mouth on
a nipple the way babies,
with fingers like cloves
of dandelion trailing

swollen bosom,
aroused skin,
hooked areola, sucked,
swallowed, took me in.

These breasts no longer
work like bees
at the mere thought
of a newborn's

squirming weight
close to the hive
rooting like swarms
in fields of clover.

Collapsed now,
sagging, my
honeycomb ducts
wish to open

for man,
baby, sun,
seed, roots,
earth as mouth.

Joanne Allred/Early Light

Swathes of mist gauze the hillside where
Two white-rumped forms the size of jackrabbits
Bound in the tall, drying grass.
Laid back ears.

From behind the brush a doe appears.
She dips her head to nuzzle
The smaller fawn and allows
Them both to suckle.

There's a story of a Tibetan monk, at last
Complete and poised to merge with the infinite,

Who, with his final breath, remembers
A stag in a field at sunrise
And instantly incarnates as a deer.

The doe is on the move now. Her fawns
Totter after, prancing every few steps
To keep up. They browse
Into the woods and vanish.

Was it the soul's yearning after beauty
That drew the dying man back into a body?

Or did his heart crack open,
As mine just did, wanting somehow
To keep this fleet tenderness.

Joanne Allred/Bleat

One day in late May they are suddenly gone,
Six spring lambs we've tracked, the dogs
And I, on our walks past their field.

I've made a habit of counting, a game
Of spotting them hidden beneath the willows
Where they liked to lie in a heap or
In the sheltering lee of their dams' shadows.

How quickly they fattened on milk
And sweet meadow grass, from spindly-
Legged wobblers to gamboling wool balls,
Nearing half the size of their mothers.

The three shorn ewes remain, heads
Bent to earth where the graze
Is already browning. One stands apart,

Lifting to gaze around through dumb,
Slotted eyes, her teats still sagging.
Her bleat is a knell—the sound
Of absence, of grief, of unrelieved need,

The wild and delicate interiors of old hungers.

Susan Richardson/A River Runs

I am a branch: *of many tines.*
I am a wash: *hung up to dry.*
A channel too: *upon a switch.*
Could be a marsh: *no opposition brook.*
I am a bed: *where flowers grow.*
I am a great depression: *blue.*
Have been a draw: *whom artists sketch.*
Also a sag: *in a much-used bed.*
I am a burn: *the fertile field.*
I am a run: *to victory!*
And as a creek: *my long hair streams,*
Will be the shallow arm: *which grasps the sea.*
I am the mirror *on which the sun*
Lays down the old oak's heavy head.

Bart Galle/Love in the Time of Global Warming

My love for you is as vast as the polar ice cap.
As soon as I say that, you know
where this is going. You read the papers,
watch specials on CNN or National Geographic
with their satellite views of the shrunken mass
inside the full embrace of what used to be.
But more to the point, you've seen the polar bears
die swimming in the open ocean
looking for the food that once sustained them,
how they sink, suddenly human with their front paws up
and waving, then curl inward, tumbling into darkness.
You might say what's left is still worth saving,
unimaginably deep, not fully explored, recoverable
if we just control a few bad habits.
And the beauty of light through that emerald ice—
how can we give that up?
It's just those chunks falling off each day, the pain
of watching them float away.

Crystal Charee/De-Nox

Enchanted by her maddened Siren's croon,
Compelled to follow, yearning hard to hide,
Within her dank, her dark, her damned lagoon.

You chased the barb and bony tongue, but soon
She stole your breath, enthralling, stunning bride,
Enamored with her maddened Siren's croon.

In murk arose sad burbles—madness strewn,
Your mind and body tumbled by the tide,
Within her dank, her dark, her damned lagoon.

Your cry was why I'd kept my ear attuned,
Salvation came too late. I watched—you died.
Ensorcelled by her maddened Siren's croon.

I bore you, taught you fresh and cheeky tunes,
Inspiring gladness. Lonely, she resides
Within her dank, her dark, her damned lagoon.

You glow with potent spirit that was hewn
From thralldom foiled, defeated, and defied.
No longer captured by her Siren's croon,
Within her dank, her dark, her damned lagoon.

Phyllis Carol Agins/Flash!

I know Henry is in trouble even before the phone rings. The sirens sound from far off, narrowing until they collect at the corner. Only five minutes before, the lights flickered as the promised cold front passed overhead. Just before the lightning exploded like some malfunctioning strobe light darting in front of my eyes. And then the sirens.

The rain mixes with my sweat as I run down the block, while the neighbors watch from their porches. There's disaster coming down the street.

"Henry," I breathe.

Four ambulances and a fire truck wait in front of the house. A line of men already stretches across the driveway, ready to turn people away.

"You gotta stay back, lady," a cop tells me.

"The man who lives here," I manage, "he's family."

The front door is axed open. Beyond, the curtains flap furiously. Henry's TV is still on, turned to the Weather Channel with the crawling line warning of tornadoes and severe lightning. As if I need to be told.

I find the knot of men in the back yard. A tree by the chain-link fence blazes in spite of the rain. The men move aside, and I watch them working on Henry.

"I saw him fall," Elsie, his neighbor, cries. "He ran out just when the storm was passing, and I saw him tumble back like someone pushed him on the chest."

There's a look of surprise on Henry's blue face—something like *Oh.* And wonderment as to what's coming next. His hands are stretched open, and they're blackened, with strange lines marching across his palms, writing a message I should read aloud. He's still wearing his slippers, even though he's splayed out like a crucifixion.

"We're trying to bring him back," a medic tells me.

"A guy should know better than to go out in a storm," someone insists.

"All for dry clothes." Another shakes his head.

I look up because Henry's face is trying to tell me something. But he's with my mother now, or maybe that's how I like to think about the end of my own life—as if I had someone to join. No one since my husband left town after the divorce with only the occasional card sent to the kids to prove that their father still exists. Some years I get a birthday card too.

But heaven's invisible, and I focus on the here and now, like Henry's very wet clothing still pinned to the line. Flowered sheets lie on the ground next to him. I remember when my mother bought them, not long after her marriage.

"You'll see, honey," she had promised me. "You'll find someone, too." That was ten years ago.

Henry complained about those sheets, but even after we buried her, he was still sleeping on them, as though he might find my mother hidden within the flowers, alive and warm next to him.

Then the fine metal line crosses my eyes. Pockmarked by clothespins, the line stretches across the garden from tree to tree, anchored with Henry's special knots. *Why that would support a man crawling from rooftop to rooftop,* he bragged. *It'll last for years.*

"We figure he grabbed onto the line just as the lightning struck," a medic tells me. "The bolt nailed the tree over there and traveled through his arms to his heart."

Henry would like this end. There's no military band playing, no parade forming, but that was a big bang, for sure. Like the gods blasted a cannon to drag him from the Earth.

The medics slowly pull away, and I feel that my own heart has stopped.

Elsie is crying. "Such a good man. So kind and helpful."

I kneel by Henry and try to wipe the rain out of his face before covering him with my mother's sheet. I'm walking to the steps when I hear the men gasp. Or maybe that noise is coming from somewhere else, like a soul flying overhead in its first wild freedom ride. I turn back to see Henry sitting up healthy and pink, still wearing the sheet like an unneeded shroud.

"What did I miss?" he asks Elsie.

I wonder how Henry is going to manage.

Inside, I'm terrified that I'll have to do the good stepdaughter thing and take care of him too. How can I? With a full-time job typing legal briefs and my three kids. What if Henry starts talking Army language and the house is filled with "F" words that I have to shoo out the window like a batch of biting flies? What if he can't button his shirt or zip his fly after peeing all over the floor? What if.

I'm panicked while I wait to see how the lightning has jolted Henry's brain. The CAT scan looks like normal brains to me—nothing scrambled or out of place.

"Watch him closely," the doctor says. "We'd admit him, but he insists on going home. He's worried about the laundry."

At that point, I'm hopeful since Henry sounds like himself. He lets me take him by the arm. I buckle his seat belt like he's my kid because his hands are wound with bandages.

Before, Henry was on Army schedule even after he retired. He kept his hair clipped short and raised the flag each day. On national holidays he planted dozens of small flags along the edges of his yard. Every morning his blinds were up by eight. In summer, garden watering was finished by 8:30. In winter, snow removal was finished by nine, even when he reached his 80s. Finally, he'd allow himself that first cup of coffee.

After Mom died, Henry's schedule stayed the same. But when I passed Henry's after some lousy blind date that a friend swore would be with the love of my life, the lights stayed on all night. Because no matter what the cost, he must have been afraid of the loneliness the dark delivered.

Now, with bandaged hands, Henry accepts the foil-wrapped lunches the neighbor ladies offer. Elsie runs crying from the front door because something has changed.

"It's his eyes," she tells me. "They're empty when they used to support the world."

I look in Henry's eyes and see the clear whites and Paul Newman-blue disks.

"Henry," I ask him. "What's in your head these days?"

"I hear an orchestra playing," he says. "Every ten minutes the cymbals crash, and I know it's time to celebrate."

"What are you celebrating?" I ask, afraid.

"Just the beginning of time." He smiles then, and I see he's forgotten his dentures. "Send the kids over and I'll sing them a tune."

"Something we know?"

"From outta the world." He smiles again.

His empty gums make him look like someone's baby.

Five weeks after the incident, as my kids call it, the old Henry is no-where to be seen. I pay Sean, my oldest, ten dollars an hour to babysit his stepgrandpa. All he has to do is listen to Henry's new stories and tell jokes when Henry seems sad.

"He's not depressed, Mom," Sean informs me. "He's only making himself ready for when the messages arrive."

"Whatever." I'm afraid to ask more. "Just keep him safe."

Then, two months after that accident, when the leaves have started to turn, and I have to remind Sean to make Henry wear more than shorts and his flowered sheet, Sean asks for the car keys.

"He wants to make trips," my son informs me, holding his new license like an award.

"Isn't this an excuse to visit your friends?"

"Mom, I'd never lie. That's one thing Henry always taught me."

"Make sure you buckle him in," I say, as I download the bus schedule in and out of town because I still have to get to work. "And make him comb his hair."

Now, I've got two of them to worry about. Sean is driving Henry on very important business all over town. Sean is missing school and forgetting his homework because he says that Henry's mission is more important. When I try to get a definition—a mission for God? A mission for humanity? A trip into outer space?—my son nods emphatically and whispers, *Maybe all of the above.*

One night, after work, after I've typed for hours, I'm finally slipping into sleep. I hear the front door open. It's raining again, and the leaves densely pack the sidewalks and the streets—a wet carpet—worse than black ice. Every once in a while, I think I hear the vibration of thunder. I'm grateful that sleep is just beyond the next second.

Then there's Henry standing by the foot of my bed, dripping again, as though he appreciates being wet and cold. His long hair is plastered against his beard, and he's wearing his PJs and my mother's flowered sheet tacked to his shoulders like a superhero's cape.

I sit up straight in my bed. What bad news now—the thought jumps the synapses of my nerves like lightning.

"I'm finally ready," Henry says after Sean makes him a bed on the couch. He's naked under the blanket except for the towel he insists on draping over his head. *Helps with reception,* he tells me.

"Henry's about to start," Sean announces.

Start what? I'm afraid to ask.

On the next Saturday, Henry decides on the statue of Joan of Arc, just across from the Art Museum. She's been gilded gold and rides happily for the glory of God. She looks excited even though she'll soon be burned to dust, betrayed both by man and her deity.

Somehow people line up like waiting for the next coming attraction.

Henry tells a woman that her dog has kidney stones, and she has to change his diet. He tells a pregnant woman that the twins will be born six weeks early but will be just fine. He tells a wife that her husband needs to see the doctor before three o'clock that afternoon. He informs a woman that her son is going to Iraq. She runs home crying. For six hours Henry speaks to strangers. By the end of the afternoon, a group is sitting quietly at his feet waiting for the next message.

"Why are you doing this?" I ask him.

"My new job," he replies. "The one I was born for."

"You always said you were born to be a soldier."

"That was for my first birthday," Henry insists. "This job is after my second."

"You mean the day you almost died?"

"I did die," Henry says seriously. "And I can tell you it's an experience not to be missed."

The next Saturday, Henry positions himself by the statue of Don Quixote. I think he favors saints on horseback. This one is anemic, like he needs the kind of meal Henry used to consume. But hasn't Henry started to look like the Don, aesthetic, stringy, driven by his own brand of madness?

People come with questions and gifts. The police arrive to organize the crowd, but there's really no need. The offerings are piled up—flowers and pet hamsters, hair ribbons and clucking chickens, fish fried in banana leaves, molasses-baked beans, and packs of cigarettes. There's a hat with feathers, a still-frozen turkey, bagels loaded with sesame seeds, and leeks crowned with foot-long greens. The offerings rest in baskets around Henry's feet, a farmer's market where there was only trash. Don Quixote searches the sky, and Henry reads the bronze face before he dispenses the truth.

One by one, the people ask their questions, and, patiently, Henry speaks. With each answer, Henry's curly hair blossoms around his head like a halo. When he speaks, his voice pounds like thunder.

Even I'm impressed. But I don't ask about my life. About my lack of dreams and my endless loneliness. I figure if Henry's got something to tell me, he can pick his moment since he lives at the house all the time now.

Even Elsie approves. "Your mother would be proud of you." She weeps a little as puts her arm around my shoulders. "You're a good woman."

The day passes in a minute. Volunteers have collected the offerings for the homeless, and Henry doesn't even look tired. When I buckle him in the car, he watches me with Henry's old eyes.

"Cecile," he says to me, "your happiness is just around the corner. But first you need to climb Mount Olympus."

I start to answer that I don't have the time, but Henry interrupts my thoughts.

"Try the Art Museum." Henry is smiling toothlessly, and those blue eyes laugh at some truth only he can read.

The museum is cool and quiet in the middle of the week. I've taken a sick day because, somehow like the others, I've grown to believe Henry's truth. Henry said to wander, and so I will.

I stand at the grand staircase. A breeze blows down the stairs and plays with my hair that I've just colored because Henry's words have given me hope. I've even worn a dress that ignores my thick waist and accentuates my bosom. *Just in case*, I've told myself. I want to be ready just in case Henry is right.

I follow the breeze like a thread into the gallery on the second floor. In front of me, I find the small bronze balanced on the marble pedestal. Bearded and muscular like a young man, the god Jupiter jabs at the sky with his pointed finger, threatening to summon the lightning he'll toss to earth. His hair flows behind him as though he's commanded a great wind.

I lean closer, pulled by whispers I can't decipher that finally roar behind my ears. They are calling me—here, here—and I look closer. And then, below the raised finger, a familiar face grins down at me.

"Why, Henry—it's you!"

I laugh so loudly that the gallery rings out with that strong and bold and very new voice I have, at last, discovered.

Joanne Lowery/Anesthesia

A man in a disposable cap asks me questions,
says it will take only ten seconds for me to cross
from this pain to a new one. I lie in a gown
blue as Mary's, a woman beloved by millions
even when she closed her eyes. I don't mind
a short sleep, this sandman a stranger in a paper hat.
He writes on his clipboard with a hand less beautiful
than the one that once pointed to a mushroom
growing in a southern Illinois forest. We did not touch
the Angel of Death, its marble flesh disguised as innocence,
its desire to punish amateurs. I was tempted to sneak a piece
home in my pocket for the day I knew love was gone
to prove if he was right. Or there and then
take a bite and watch his face,
give him something to regret every morning
when he woke up, as I will, when the doctors are done
and a nurse tells me only an hour is gone.

Joanne Lowery/Kneading

She was making bread when a bullet
came in through the north window
and tunneled through her back.
Her hands fell away from the lump of dough,
the bullet let out a cheer, a sigh,
and in the confusion the dough rose a little more.

She never knew whether anyone finished
turning it into an elastic oval
and set it in the oven for fifty minutes.
What war would historians call this,
who would get the dates of her headstone right?
Her fingers died sticky with flour
and her apron front bloomed red.

It's not good to waste food, so let's pray
for the bread. It's not wise to waste bullets,
so let's rejoice that this stray found a home.
She was feeding the enemy and now the dough
would lie heavy as stone on the table.
What the house smelled of was not yeast
and goldenness, and the room no longer rocked
with the push and pull of her deftness.
Grief pounded the loaf into submission,
sorrow spread butter on the first slice.

Scott Owens/Dead of Winter

In November they drain the lake,
sucking away the color like dead
leaves, smashing the mirror of still
water, exposing wishful pennies,
sunken floats, mud-crusted golf
balls, an old leader on thin line.

The central stream, hidden origin
before the dam, reappears on the bottom,
a brown jug of earth. Islands of sludge,
old tires, Christmas trees long forgotten
jut up to be recognized
in their winter of showing.

The ducks grow quiet, skimming the thin
surface, swimming the shrinking
vein of water shared with what remains
of turtle, fish, and gull, each thing
moving among the ripples of itself.

These days anyone can play Christ,
walking on the absence of water,
the kept shape of lake.

Scott Owens/Common Knowledge

Let's read the leaves again, the ashes,
the bones thrown against the ground.
Let's find our lover's name in the peel
of an apple kept whole in cutting.
Let's burn the afterbirth, count the pops
it makes as children not yet born.

Each thing echoes the life it knows.
The trees sing of wind and rain,
the sky predicts the weather,
and who knows what words well up
in the ground, push to be heard
above the sound of coins dropped
like wishes. We know the birds
speak of love, the bees of travel
and labor. We know that one crow
is sorrow, two crows joy. We know
a flower can tell the difference
between love and love me not,
a willow branch can hum its way
to water, and a single red leaf
can speak of a season of burning,
of the whole earth going up
in red and gold. Even a lover
rocking speechless in the arms
of another makes a noise his body knows
as words. Stop. Stand still. Listen.
There is no end to what we might learn.

Nancy Kassell/Liturgy of the Cell

Between a.m. cliché and p.m. cacophony,
I am consumed by the concentricity of events,
stone skipped across smooth waters.

In every scale, major and minor,
I question the dominant chord,
listen for the *sotto voce* of first morning birdsong,
which has taught me cadence;
listen for the surge of bloom—
phlox, parsley, conifer.

Blood flows in a continuous loop;
stem cells are turned on to appointed tasks,
and at intervals, the subtlety of a diminished seventh.

Every mode reveals the sky.

These are the whole notes:
       Calculate your carbon footprint.
       Scour your conscience.

The century, though young, thrums loudly.

Arin Keshishian/Ludwig

Skins stretch out to spread
across hollow space,
awaiting heartbeats
to happen again.

Lugs feel like ribs
planted on coarse maple body,
where metal rims stick out—
fingernails around your integument.

When music plays,
snare wires buzz
from soothing vibrations.
You can't help vocalizing.

Speak rock in 4/4.
Speak blues in 3/4.

Express tone, structure, time
through slow wear and tear
conducted by the master.

Crash and ride,
ride and crash—
But always keep the pace,
elegant flare.

Lights fall, melted butter
adds gold on tanned wings.
Emanating sounds spread
bouncing resonance.

RATATA RADA BOOM BA PSSSSSSsss. . .
Hickory sticks hit, tap, swat;

seasoning's added
under yellowbright glare.

The stool puffs up,
caressed softly with plain cloth
to rid sweat,
durable placidity.

Cranked for tune
in clockwise motion,
gradual circle
completes eternity.

Mary Christine Delea/Rip Current

Slung into one with you, no ratchet is needed,
just balance and clean lines, corners cut right,
beams heavy and strong.

I never question why currents run the way they run,
dependent on so many things: other currents, smooth beds,
rocks, weather and what humans make—

construction and destruction. No tools we invent
could help me understand the force
of the river, or of creation.

I bring skill to this job, you bring labor and
a strong work ethic. We both share a love of water,
and can swim against anything.

This is marriage: place a socket here, hammer out
your troubles, nail me to the sails.
Water can't wash us away,

and if we stop building, we will only melt away
what we have built together. Our hands are rough,
but we are smart enough to know

that when things come too easily
there is always trouble ahead, whether we are
wading or making a raft.

Donald Sheehy/Of Trees

I hear nothing of me
in the flourish of leaves
in the soft susurrus
that sift from a breeze
or the loud ululations
when wind whips the trees.

I feel nothing of me
in the strength of the bole
in the hard rectitude
that heartwood holds
as the bark is scarred
into fissure and fold.

Our likeness, I suspect,
lies half-hidden in soil
where a shallow surface root
gropes in the dark and coils,
gathering and holding close
each stone that foiled its way.

Sheila Tombe/Tower

        no avenue of repose, no tree-
lined summer street down which to wander, safe;
no catalogue of missed conformities to chance,
nor design against catastrophe or charm.
No ecstasies. No gathered linen waist-
line, no composed responses to the call;
no fingered pages turned to contemplate
the masters' words of comfort or of pain;
no agony. No lingering complaints, no
shrill enforcement of salvation's grasp
against the grain of finger-slipping loss.
No return. No way out
other than through the narrow eye of night
unfocused and alone. No knowledge nor remorse
nor anger nor control. No single effort lost
without the wrenching certainty of fear
enveloped in a heartland hymn of hope.
No reply to the question lovingly lowered
on a rope of soul-spun thread that yearns
for just a scrap, a taste, a syllable, a touch
not contaminated by the dust of mayhem.
No answer.

John Azrak/Love Times Zero

I would give up a friend to follow in Baryshnikov's
    footsteps for a day. I'd give up another to get

through *Finnegan's Wake*, one more to have Dylan
    sing "Visions of Johanna" in my company.

To write my own tune, I'd stand up the lover who
    meets me downtown when it's time to get outside

of myself. I'd forsake the teacher who started
    sentences I could finish and graced me with his

kind presence if I could sketch your beautiful
    face with a steady hand. I'd desert the life-

long friend who left his fingerprints on my
    soul when I was sure I hadn't one if

I could live inside the paint that makes
    the canvas whisper nothing is more real

than nothing with you gone. To straddle the abyss
    alone, walk the line between here and not,

I'd multiply who I give up by what will never be.

James Pate/**Parrot**

She didn't make it a mystery, why she left me. I was thin and barely ever ate. I had colds for half the year. I bought expensive imported beer I couldn't afford. I did have a job, but it wasn't a good one. And when it came to food, I liked watching cooking shows on Cable, but even when I made something simple like French toast, I fucked it up. Made it taste too salty. "I didn't know it was possible to screw up French toast by adding too much salt," she said. She made a lot of good points. When she said she was leaving, I was happy for her. It happened in October. I called up to rent the moving van. We didn't talk much as I helped her take her furniture from our place. Things were awkward. I kept being overly nice to her, and she kept giving me a suspicious look. Her fat brother helped us. That made it more awkward. Her fat brother had never been much of a fan of mine. He'd eye me as if being thin was a disease he didn't want to catch.

It was hard work altogether. We took plenty of smoke breaks. Besides being thin, I have a weak back. So I had to take more breaks than they did.

After the sofa there was only one more thing. That was the bird: her expensive parrot that was about as smart as an animal could be. She'd paid an entire month's salary for the creature long before I knew her. And she'd let it fly around free, when the windows were closed. She was putting the blanket over its cage when I asked her, "You sure about this?"

"Do I in any way look unsure?" she asked me back. All I had to do would be look out the window at the loaded van to answer that.

"You need any money?" I asked, though I didn't have any to spare.

She looked at me like she knew that too. "I'm fine," she said.

Jake drove. Sarah sat with the cage on her lap in the passenger's seat. I waved to them, but neither one of them waved back. They were looking out, at the road, and not at me. I walked out through the yard and over to the sidewalk, watching the van go down the street. By the time it finally turned at the end of the street, I realized I'd wandered out to the middle of the road. I was standing there with my hands in my jacket pockets, shivering. It was only when I went back inside and saw the place where the sofa had been and the wall where the TV had stood did I begin to realize that I wasn't just shivering with cold. I was sick. My forehead was burning up.

The next morning, I called in sick to work. I sprayed houses for a pest control company. At other times and in other places I'd been a cab driver, a security officer, and a dog groomer. But around the time Sarah left, I was working at the pest control company.

Carla answered the phone. She was the stepdaughter of Mr. Morgan, the guy who owned the small company. Sometimes she acted as a secretary when the real secretary was busy. She didn't work with the company officially, but some mornings she came in and helped out. "You sound like you've been swallowing shards of glass," she told me. "Get some rest, all right?"

I hung up the phone and stared at the blank space along the wall where the TV had been. I knew it would be a dull, awful day. I tried to sleep. But when it turned noon, and I found myself still awake, I pulled a chair up to the kitchen table and started drinking and thinking about Sarah. About her blond hair and about the purple dress she used to wear on certain Saturday nights. By the time the next day came around, I was actually glad to go to work.

I heard about Carla's situation from a guy I sometimes went out to lunch with. He worked for Mr. Morgan too, spraying houses as I did. There was a Thai place on Cleveland Avenue we both liked. It had a buffet with amazing pad thai and pad prik. No other Thai place in Memphis compared. Ed would show up in his muddied coveralls, looking like a hundred year old with his hornrimmed glasses and stringy gray hair. "Carla's getting a divorce," he said one afternoon. It was about a week after Sarah left.

"She just got married," I said.

"Yeah. Too quickly as it turns out."

"She had her ring on this morning."

"That's for show. She likes looking like she's married."

I'd barely ever seen Ed talking to Carla. The way he was talking, you'd think he was her beloved uncle. "And how did you come about all this information?"

"I heard her on the phone a few days back."

"That must've been some conversation."

"I wasn't eavesdropping. I don't do that."

"I'm not judging."

"If I hear something, I can't help it."

I took a bite of the pad prik. It was so good it made the back of my head feel like it was exploding in slow motion.

"I always thought she was pretty," I said.

"Jesus, Rick. The girl just got divorced."

That was Friday. On Saturday I kept thinking about her. She was my age, around forty or so; she was pretty, with large sad eyes and hairy eyebrows. In fact, I loved her eyebrows. Sarah would pluck her brows, and it'd drive me crazy. It'd give her a haunted and severe look. But Carla looked lovely with those brows. They made her black eyes stand out all the more. By Sunday I'd talked myself into thinking that I should ask her out for a drink. That would sound innocent enough. A drink. If it turned into a date, so be it. Of course, the asking part scared me. All too easily I could see her saying no and telling the other people in the company what I'd done, and soon I'd start feeling like I was being made fun of behind my back. *There's the jerk that tried to ask me out a few days after my divorce. Said he wanted to go for a drink. A drink!* By Monday, though, I thought I'd do it anyway. Watching Sarah leave had put me in a reckless mood. And listening to her reasons for leaving had made me want to better myself. Take a risk or two.

Days I didn't eat at the Thai place, I'd eat a cheese sandwich in the break room. It was a dismal little space. It had two plastic tables and an old poster detailing the life of the cockroach and no windows. There had once been a plant in it. The poor thing had died. I don't know whose idea it was to put a plant in a room with no windows. But Carla ate in that room every day. The rumor was she was as cheap as her stepfather, and never ate out if she could help it. I also knew she ate early. Long before most people were thinking about lunch. Monday, I saw in her there, and I took my sandwich from my desk and went in there myself. "Pretty early for you to be eating, isn't it?" she asked when I went in.

"I've got a lot of appointments this afternoon. This might be my last chance."

"You've been working hard since you've been sick."

"Really?" It took me by surprise, her saying that. It was so clearly untrue.

"Well, maybe not hard. But more than usual." She grinned. She sipped from her mug. I glanced at her hand. The ring was gone.

"You feeling better?" she asked.

"For the most part." I felt myself pause before I forced myself to say what I said next. "My girlfriend left the day I got sick. My girlfriend Sarah.

That was probably the reason I got sick in the first place."

Carla thought about this. She swallowed down more coffee. She said, "That's some tough luck. It's not fun, dealing with that shit at our age. Not that we're all that old," she added.

I nodded, agreeing. I looked at my sandwich. I hated eating that early in the morning. The sandwich had the appeal of a piece of cold plastic.

"Ed said you might have something to ask me?"

I glanced up from my sandwich. "Exactly how close are you with Ed?"

"I barely know him. Why's that?"

"Nothing. Never mind."

"Rick, what do you have going on tomorrow tonight?"

My heart turned into a fist. It really did. A fist. "Nothing at all," I told her.

"There's a bar I like to go to on Tuesday nights sometimes. It's called The Beer Haven. You ever hear of it?"

"I've heard of it." The place had wooden boards across the windows so that no one could see in. I'd never been inside. But I had friends who had. They talked about the smell of it and the way you could barely see to the end of the room due to how dark it was. Mostly rednecks hung out there. A few college kids.

"You want to go? They've got the cheapest drinks in town."

I felt numb. That was how overcome I was. I wanted to kiss her eyebrows.

"If it's cheap, hell yeah. I'd do anything if it's cheap."

I made myself shut up before I blabbered on. She drank from her mug and stood. "See you then," she told me. She went up to the front desk to answer the phone that was ringing.

I have a tendency to arrive at most places late. But I got to The Beer Haven early. I parked in the narrow lot behind the row of storefronts where the bar was located and listened to an oldies radio station and watched for Carla's car. Finally I saw it in my driver's mirror. I went over to the car and hugged her when she came out. She wore a pretty blue necklace made with blue strings that'd been wrapped around one another and a few beads that held the pieces together. It looked Asian. It really looked pretty on her. I complimented it. "An old boyfriend gave it to me," she said.

"He had good taste."

"Yeah. That and nothing else."

We entered through the back door. The smell grabbed me right away. It was the smell of beer and old cigarette smoke and dog piss and shit. I'd never been in a public place that'd smelled like that; it didn't seem like it'd be legal. Later on in the night I realized that The Beer Haven had a dog that lived in it. A poor mutt with three working legs and a fourth that looked like a twig. The staff of The Beer Haven didn't do a great job taking the animal on walks. You could tell because of the shit stains on the carpet. (And that was another thing—a carpet. I'd never been in a bar with carpeting, and shag carpeting at that.) It was about as dark as I imagined it too. There were some lights over the bar, and each booth had a little light, but that was it.

We sat at one of those booths. Carla got in on my side. The waitress that showed up at our table was an elderly woman wearing big glasses with white frames. Carla seemed to know her.

Know her and not like her. "So what will you two be having?" she asked. She had the tone of a nurse at the end of an exhausting shift.

"You have Gulden Draak?" I asked.

"A golden what?"

"Gulden Draak. It's a Belgium beer."

She looked at Carla with pure contempt, as if to say, This is the kind of trash you bring into this place now? "Mister," she said, turning to me, "if you want something like that I really suggest you go someplace else."

"We will both have a Budweiser," Carla told her.

She nodded to herself. She left.

"She's been working here too long," Carla said.

"She's not going to spit in our beers, is she?"

"I wouldn't put it past her."

"Shit."

"The beer really is cheap here."

"God, I'd sure hope so."

She placed her hand on my leg. She tapped her fingertips across my knee. The gesture was more nervous than sexy. I took her hand and held it. We started talking about Sarah. About her ex-husband. We complained about them, said they were losers. But I was lying. I never thought Sarah was a loser. When she walked out the door, I'd wanted to go with her.

The beers came. We drank them quickly. I can't stand Budweiser, but I still drank it quickly. We ordered some more. I hadn't really gotten drunk since the day after Sarah had left, when I'd sat at the kitchen table with a bottle of bourbon. But I wanted to get drunk that night. I needed to. I had to. I even missed Sarah's parrot. I wanted to get so drunk when I closed my eyes it'd be like the night sky spinning around. I wanted to feel sick in the morning. And I wanted to do all that with Carla. With her getting every bit as drunk as me.

We had another two beers each. Then, we were hugging and kissing. I kept rubbing my face along her neck. Her perfume smelled like sliced oranges. Her hair was curly and frazzled and it tickled my cheek. I knew other people were staring, probably nudging one another. There were lanky guys around the bar playing some drinking contest. By the pool table a huge man in overalls danced with a small woman whose long hair almost fell to her knees. I didn't care about any of them.

Carla had to use the restroom. As she walked away, I noticed a guy I hadn't noticed before. He stood in the corner. He held a pool cue. He had a black baseball cap on his head and he wore tinted glasses. His lambchop sideburns came down to his chin. From the way he looked at Carla go toward the restrooms, I knew he knew her.

Then he looked at me. He smiled a mean little smile. For the first time that night I wished I wasn't as drunk as I was.

Carla returned.

The man put the cue in the rack and took the seat across from us and took off his black baseball cap. He had a big forehead and thinning hair. He grinned, showing us his big, ugly teeth.

"Carla," he said, "it is mighty fine to see you."

Carla looked surprised. But not overly surprised. "Hey, Junior. It's been a long time."

"Too long."

"I wouldn't say that. Just long enough."

He turned to me, still grinning that grin. Still showing those teeth. I couldn't tell his age. His thinning hair might have made him appear older than he was. "This is my very good friend Rick," she told him. "Rick, this is Junior."

He stuck his hand out. He shook with a firm grip, his eyes staring right into my eyes. "I'm always glad to meet one of Carla's friends," he told me. "Any friend of Carla's I immediately consider a friend of mine."

I put my arm back around Carla's shoulders. "That's very generous of you," I said.

"If I was interrupting something, I can always leave."

I thought about saying he sure as hell was interrupting something, but I didn't want to be petty. Not in front of Carla. So I waited for what Carla would say. "Yeah, you can stay for a drink I guess." She looked up to see if the waitress was nearby. She wasn't. Carla said, "If I remember correctly, you owe me some money."

"That train ticket from here to New Orleans."

"That would be it."

"Carla, darling, you haven't even asked what I was doing down there."

I asked for her. "What were you doing down there, Junior?"

He did that smile again. His wide lambchops made him look like an admiral in an old movie. I decided he was a terrible person.

"All sorts of wonderful things. Some of it above the table. Some of it under."

"That's kind of vague."

"It's best if I kept it like that."

Carla squeezed my hand. "Rick, here's the story. We used to date. Ages ago. It was no big deal. And we've been friends ever since."

"I've never heard you describe me as a friend, Carla."

"That waitress sure is taking forever," I said.

"You're not a foe, I guess," Carla told him. "So what else would I call you?"

Junior stared around. He looked at the waitress, who stood three tables down, with her back to us. She'd made a real effort to ignore us all night long. "Listen. Why don't y'all come over to my place? I have a new apartment. I moved out from Mama's last week. It ain't much. But it's quieter than here. And I have the money there. I would've brought it with me, but I wasn't sure you'd actually be here."

Carla looked at me; I could tell she wanted me to be the one to say yes. "All right," I agreed.

Carla rubbed my knee and said, "That sounds good. No funny business, though. All right, Junior?" Junior grinned and nodded no. I didn't know what she meant by "funny business," and now I was starting to regret having gone out at all.

In the parking lot Carla asked me to drive. She was more drunk than I was. She was cold too. I gave her the jacket I kept behind my seat in the truck. She wrapped it around herself, put her hands in its pockets, and leaned over on me. I followed Junior's old Nissan through Overton Park, which was deserted except for the male prostitutes who stood under some of the trees, watching us go by, and out on to Madison Avenue. It was late. The street was pretty empty. We followed Junior into the parking lot of an apartment building. There was graffiti on some of the walls. "Home is where the heart is," Junior said as he led us up the stairs to his place. Neither me nor Carla said a thing.

The inside was even more empty than the house that waited for me on the other side of town. There were some plastic chairs along the wall. A paper plate with a crumpled napkin sat on one of the chairs. There was no carpeting, and the floorboards were buckled in places and rough-looking. "I hope some rum will do you," Junior told us.

I didn't want to drink anything that'd been sitting in those rooms. "None for me, thanks," I said, and I pulled one plastic chair up to another and sat in it. Carla sat in the other. The wind was high, whipping against the windows.

"I'll have some," Carla said. "And no ice. You use too much ice."

Junior stepped into the kitchen and stepped back out with the bottle and two plastic cups. He gave me a smile I didn't like. "You sure you don't want anything?" he asked. "There's water too, if you're thirsty."

"I'm fine."

That was when I heard the groan for the first time. Behind where Junior was sitting, pouring the two drinks, there was a doorway which led to the hall. There were Mardi Gras beads hanging from that doorway. The groan came from somewhere down that hall. "You have company?" I asked him.

"A friend of mine. Must be napping."

Carla stared at him but didn't say anything. He handed her the drink, and she put it on the floor without sipping it. She had her hand on the armrest of my chair. "This place is even worse than your other places, Junior. Maybe you should've stayed at your mom's until you found something better," she said.

"Did you ever meet Mom?"

"I did. I didn't like her."

"That sounds like you."

"Where's my money, Junior?"

"Relax. We're having a good time, aren't we?" He turned to me. "Except for this guy. You've been looking like a sad sack since I met you."

"Leave him alone. His girlfriend just left him."

I hated her telling him that. "I left her too," I lied. "It was mutual."

"Women are bitches. All of them but my mother."

"I'm a bitch?" Carla asked. It was like she was daring him to say yes.

"And you, Carla. My mother and you."

There was the groan again. It was a woman's groan. A young woman.

"She has a lot of nightmares and she winds up groaning in her sleep," Junior tried to explain. "I usually end up sleeping in here. I let her have the bed. I can't help but be a gentleman sometimes." He turned to me again. "Did you love her?"

"I guess I didn't love her enough." I was lying again.

"I'm sorry for you."

"Thanks."

"Don't mention it."

No one said anything, and the wind kept whipping against the windows. I knew that tomorrow the trees would look different. Many of the yellow and gold leaves would be stripped away from them and the branches would begin to look the way they did during winter. Junior took off his hat, rubbed his hand through his hair, seemed to think for a moment, and roughly placed his hat back on his head. He turned to me. "That necklace she's wearing is from me," he said. "I gave it to her when she turned twenty-one. We went out drinking that night and didn't get home until morning."

"That was a long time ago," said Carla.

The room was beginning to feel very small and dirty.

"I need to get going," I told Carla.

She gave my arm a squeeze. "Wait until he gives me my money."

"Junior, you want to go ahead and do that? You want to pay her so we can get out of here?" That moaning scared me. It wasn't a simple moan. And she didn't sound asleep.

He finished his whiskey and leaned back and parted the beads with his hand and looked down the hallway. Then he turned back to us. He smiled and said to me, "Did Carla ever tell you I once killed a guy? It was in self-defense, and I got off. It was a burglar trying to get in my house. Some junkie kid. I blew him away with my rifle."

"And why exactly would you be bringing this up?"

"Because he's an asshole," Carla said.

"Right. Because I'm an asshole. But also because I think it's something people should know about me."

It was like I could feel the blood in my hands and arms. I suddenly missed Sarah terribly. I wanted to leave that apartment and go home to her. But I couldn't. Her clothes didn't hang in my closet anymore. Her watch wouldn't be ticking on the bedside table. Ticking away in the dark. I asked Junior, "You saying this as some kind of a threat?"

"No, buddy. I'm actually not." He gave me a look that seemed to say he was serious about that. "I'm saying it because I want you to understand me."

Then came the moan again. It was too much, simply sitting there. I stood and zipped up my jacket. "I'm leaving," I told Carla. "He's not going to give you the money."

"He's right, Carla. I'm not. I don't have it. I spent all the money I made in Louisiana, and as you can tell I'm not exactly living in luxury here."

Carla had her eyes on him. "You really are too much," she murmured. She swallowed hard. I took her hand, the one that had been on my armrest, but she took it away from me. She stood up. She would not stop looking at him.

Junior returned her look. I might as well not have been in the room. "That girl down there is a whore," he told her. "How does that make you feel, Carla? She's a crack whore. She groans like that because she's fucking baked out of her mind all the time."

Carla took her purse from the floor and we began moving toward the door. Junior stayed in his chair. Started calmly pouring himself another cup of rum. The last thing I heard before we went out the door was, "She's amazing, Carla. She's a crack whore and she does something to me you never did." He laughed. "You know exactly what I mean, don't you?"

As I closed the door he was still talking. It sounded like he was still sitting with us in there. We walked out into the parking lot, into where the wind was really blowing around, scattering leaves around the parked cars. I hated cool weather. It was worse than cold weather.

We got into my truck. "Where to now?" I asked.

She said, "Drop me off at my car. I'm done for the night. I'm sorry."

I was relieved. I was done for the night too.

We didn't talk on the ride back to The Beer Haven. But as we neared the bar, she told me, "We only dated for a short time, less than a year, but

I was young, and it made a big impression on me. I've been trying to get him out of my life for twenty years now."

"He really made an impression on me tonight too."

"He'll do that."

"Is there some really big thing wrong with him? Or is it a lot of little things?"

"He's not as bad as he seems. He seems awful, but he's not."

She didn't explain. I knew she was thinking it was now none of my business. She was right; I'd known her for such a short amount of time compared to Junior.

I drove up to her car. "I'm sorry we didn't have more fun," she said.

"Who's saying I didn't have fun?"

We hugged, and she darted out and got into her car. I started turning the truck around. I didn't go home. I just drove. It was nice, going through the quiet streets. For a long time I went down one street and then another, thinking about what had happened. I just didn't want to go home to an empty house. Not yet. So I drove, barely considering where I was going. Eventually, though, I ended up in the neighborhood where Sarah had moved. It was in the Highland Heights area of the city, in a neighborhood where Mexican families lived and where my mother's family had once lived back when she and her parents first moved to the city from a small town in Mississippi. At first I drove around the streets that surrounded the street she lived on. That got boring fast. I took a deep breath. Made the turn that took me to the street she was on.

I pulled up slow. I drove the truck up to the curb across the street, leaving the engine running, the heat on. The house where she lived was a duplex. She was on the left side. I noticed she had put on her door the batch of tied-together black corn which she'd had on our door.

I remembered one day back when she had first moved in to my place. We had made love that afternoon. Then we spent the early evening getting drunk in bed and talking about our previous marriages. After a while, Sarah began to worry. She hadn't seen her parrot in hours, and she was afraid the bird might be all confused. All turned around in the new place. She sat up in bed and whistled. She called his name. "Handsome George. Handsome George, we're calling you." And in he glided, a swift creature with green feathers; he'd perched on the brass knob of the bedpost. The sight of him startled me so much I began to laugh. I wasn't used to seeing a bird so close up. I wasn't used to having it go by so near you could feel the air pass along your skin.

As I sat there, I realized I had two choices. One was to knock on her door and ask her to let me in. If she did, I'd sit on her couch and tell her about Junior and how I'd been around something really evil that night and it'd blown me away. Sickened me. I'd tell her about his smile and his teeth. The way he drank his rum. She'd start to get upset. She'd begin asking me what did all this have to do with her. And that would be when I'd ask her to marry me. I'd tell her I'd change. I'd cook her a feast that'd actually be worth eating. I'd drink cheaper beer. In a world with Juniors around, would she marry me?

She'd probably say no. I was ready for that answer.

But I would've asked her.

My other choice was never to go to her door again. And that was what I did.

Cassie Schmitz/My Father Speaks about the Dark Country

Sometimes, after work, just as the sun
is sliding into the treetops, and the sky
is red, ripped open, a bloodstream,
I'll drive past where she lives, and I can
almost see her, the light of the television,
her face flickering like a blue flame.

I think back to New Jersey—
I go into the kelp forest I have fled,
into the waters below the canopy,
my stepfather with the gun, out cold
on the stairs, the half-cooked turkey
thrown into the snow, and I wade
through columns that have never
known the light of the surface,
that were my father, and the times
my mother would sneak behind me,
take a slug at my head.

When I sleep at night I wake to find
my house is a weigh station,
and there are people passing through
my bedroom, their bodies tracing
behind them, transparent; I don't know
that I'm dreaming, and I get up
and follow them into my closet,
which turns into a bright portal,
and I feel my body thinning,
dissolving into the air like water
boiling from a kettle.

I have felt my lungs blistering
for years now, driving home at night,
looking to where she is, and sometimes

I'll remember her at the graveyard
in Elizabeth, where her own mother
is buried, the smoke rising behind her
from the oil refineries, drifting to us,
slow, like a gas leak from a basement.

Cassie Schmitz/There's Always the Bad Poem

Most times all I can get onto the page
is some ridiculous declaration,
like *I am a noodle.* I sit staring as it
blinks on the screen, the white light
like a halo, and I say aloud *yes,*
yes, I am a noodle. O but if that
were true I was born to boil,
which makes sense, really, I've felt
the static, the steam on my lips,
especially the time I told my father
he was like his mother and I boiled
a string of blisters right over his face.

I'd be strained too, the comfortable hot
sword of the water filtered from me
until I was lost in the globular pile
that is the fate of all noodles.
No more teeth made of branding metal,
just a slippery body easily buried
in the mess—Roxie, the bullet
of her brain injury still in the gun,
never loving me to begin with.

But there's that mystery of the sauce.
I don't believe I have it, no cream,
no spice, not even a tomato.
I was always better at being a plain
noodle spilling from the box, bending,
recoiling suddenly, not like a snake,
no real venom, no real shape
like a cloud on a stormy day, shifting
every time the wind comes in.

Stuart Bartow/Borges or I

Is it I who fear deathlessness, trapped
for infinite time in a fake body,
a machine, undead, alive only
in another's fiction?

A man, fastidious, not unlike Borges,
paces down a nondescript side-street
of Buenos Aires to an appointment,
his first immortality treatment.
A bored smile from the receptionist,
the doctor reassures him the procedure
will be failsafe and painless, returns
to his laboratory to prepare.

In the waiting room, he hears
discordant whispers from an adjoining room
where he discovers jack-in-the-boxes
with portholes for speakers that emit mutterings
almost like language. The boxes stir,
rustle like mussels in a sea bed.
He flees in terror.

In his notes, Borges explains his fear
of never being able to die. Why
can I not remember the story's title?
Why can't I find this fable in any anthology?

Stuart Bartow/Mute Swans

No gods in wings, it never dawned on us
to think of them as anything but swan.
Each year we watched them, cob and pen, mute
gliders, clutch of cygnets in tow, witnessed

the disappearance of their brood, snatched
one by one, dragged under by old snappers. Still,
the couple coursed the pond's mindless sweep
while the highway bound them by its reach.

To become swan seems strange till one can glean
their strength, their stern pulsation close at hand.
In this creature of muscle and fierce curve
did Leda see symmetry of Zeus or man?

Did she take swan form to twin his grace, see
through his black eyes the marsh's return?

Lory Bedikian/Kerosene

In winter, they wait.
The line veins
through city buildings,
ashen pillars.

A man pulls his collar up
the coat, thick, black.
A woman disappears
into her moleskin shawl.

There is nothing emptier
in this season than the tanks
by their feet, sour smell,
burnt oil rising from caps

twisted off. Young boys
watch each other, sit
on the frozen containers,
lumber along when it's time

to move a foot forward.
Soon, a hydrocarbon,
petroleum elixir will bring
flames to battered stoves.

There is nothing as quiet
as Yerevan, when people
stand waiting for fuel
rationed, when they yawn

through sunrise, white
clouds rise from their lips
into the sky, strata of rock,
as the coats move along,

their fingers frozen with coins.

Lory Bedikian/How They Appear

No one understands the ghosts
    we know.

They are floating hieroglyphics
    of flame.

I say to people: look further
    so you can

see their shapes, faces clear
    as thunder.

Grandmother and I sketch them
    while awake,

flashing in the midday sun
    like copper pennies.

When I leave her side the ghosts
    drag themselves

as leaves into the subway's stairwell
    and as I work

some stay with her, braiding her hair
    down our street.

I see ghosts in the ice
    of a cocktail,

see them hanging from branches
    of the willow tree.

When sounds stir in the coffee, I write
        what they creak.

How can I begin to tell disbelievers
        their names?

How can I begin to show the fear
        these ghosts know,

like the screaming crow
        flying from a hurricane?

Askold Skalsky/Ingolstadt November, 1817

Victor begins his evening like a God
before creation's twang,
stretching his baby finger to the mist,
turning the slime into a rib, a sternum
yoked to jangling vertebrae.
Tonight he's plumbing in the depthless
sewers of eternity, maneuvering
some waters into pipes
and layering the septic, dribbling flesh
out on his high table in the atelier.
He has gathered everything but light,
removed the rubbish from his shoes,
and cleaned the instruments.
But wait! The sallow flushing of the cheeks,
the rhombic neck, the barrel bones
perdurable in every part,
and then the dream—his mother
floating her dead eyeball in a flannel grave,
the kisses on her yellow lips.

Phyllis Grilikhes/Opening Folds in a Fan

upon the taste of color
in a ruddy pear
and my hands at the keyboard
into Brahms

upon people's voices
that pass without consequence
as garbage trucks roll
with rain possible

upon trying to be less wordless
as water runs in the kitchen sink
and minutes fast forward
on the clock face

upon the blueness of a blue sky
the truth of each day
and my steps in rhythm
lightly on the avenue

upon soundless wishing
and the never-ending shock
at the swift departure of days
as they slip silently away

upon my need to give voice
to the dancer within
insisting on spoonfuls and spoonfuls
of time now offered on the winter street

upon rubbed out beginnings
marked *cancel*
and how to move those moments
across the board

upon my sister's death
and the autumn
in all the leaves that fall
missing her

upon this new year without her
it goes on—
it goes on darling without you
the pain of that

upon holding the neck of the shiny horse
as the merry-go-round swirls
and turning to see—*are you watching for me*
as I come 'round?

upon the sudden brightness
of the present day
as I pick up time
and sling it forward.

Daniel Shalvardzhyan/Six-Foot Dance

We try to move but soon have lost our feet,
And enter knowing not the quips in store.
The dance that men will always fail to cheat.

With years of progress, yet the path's concrete,
Like tides of people mending sands of shore.
We try to move but soon have lost our feet.

Aware it's near like ends of common streets,
But have no fear in taking one last snore.
The dance that men will always fail to cheat.

Slow stops the most perpetual of beats,
With loads of dirt, we fade beneath the floor.
We try to move but soon have lost our feet.

These many steps have left us incomplete.
The skies remain so vast for you to soar.
The dance that men will always fail to cheat.

We hide behind a shadow so discrete,
A step this short and sweet we must adore.
We try to move but soon have lost our feet.
The dance that men will always fail to cheat.

Doug Cox/Lullaby as a Second Language

It's not just love, it's sleep
We need more than bread, more
Than light, laughter, this stale water.

We can go for weeks without
Nourishment, shelter, the warm curl
Of words breathed off our

Foreign, our motherless tongues.
It's the falling we need, sweet dreams,
& the rest. Plus, the songs just before.

Emily Ann Zietlow /Talking to John

But I heard him, Julia says quietly.

She is staring at the oak tree that shades a corner of our backyard. She spends her time underneath it now, reading, watching the breeze stir near-dead plants in our garden. Talking to John.

She called me John yesterday. She said it casually, then saw me—the other brother. Her cheeks shaded red and she turned away, her hair cloaking her face and glassy eyes. I started to tell her that it was okay, but the words took too long, and she was gone before I could say them. Then this morning I saw her sitting by the oak, her mouth moving slow, and I knew she found John somewhere else.

We sit at the dinner table with our mother, who is staring at her plate. She looks at us differently now, and Julia can't take it. She told me last week that her heart beats fast, and her throat gets tight when Mom looks into her eyes.

Your father is staying late again, Mom says. Her office closes at five, so she has no overtime to keep her away. She says little for the rest of the meal after asking about our days and begins pushing the food around her plate. At midnight, her stomach and thoughts will wake her, and she'll walk quietly to the kitchen to eat leftovers in the dark.

I thank God Julia knows not to tell her that she's been talking with our dead brother under the oak out back. Instead, she talks about summer plans and looks up at us every few minutes to see if we have anything to say. Mom stares out the window, so Julia turns to me. I smile so that she keeps talking. By the time we wash the dishes and put the leftovers back in the take-out boxes, she dries the plates in silence.

Before I retreat to my room for the night, my father gets home. Mom is asleep already. He knows this.

Sorry I'm late, he says, loosening his tie. He says this every night, but I still believe him. Sometimes I tell him about my day, but mostly I just watch while he hangs his coat in the closet and mumbles about work, scratching his head and looking lost. His dark red hair is curly and cut close to his head like mine. Purple-colored bags bulge beneath his eyes, and his cheeks seem to be caving in like my mother's. My parents are losing life.

Julia's light is still on when I come down the hall. I can hear her humming under her breath while she plays with the small figures in her dollhouse. Mom said a few weeks ago that she thought Julia should outgrow playing with dolls soon, but apologized later when she heard Julia crying behind the bathroom door.

I lean into my sister's room and say goodnight. She turns, her pajama pants barely reaching her ankles. She's going to be tall like the rest of us.

Goodnight, Sammy, she says. I start to close the door and she continues, He thinks summer ball is a good idea. I look back and open my mouth to challenge her, but she smiles and starts to move around the small furniture again, so I leave quietly.

We were older than Julia. I was born three years after John, and my parents waited eight years more until they decided to try for a girl. After he left home, he would call once a week just for Julia. She needs it, he would say, and I wondered how he knew. John had faded freckles that seemed to blend into his skin more and more every time I saw him. He never looked into his reflection and feared what people would think, while I still hate wiping away the steam on a mirror when I get out of the shower.

I go to my window and push it open. In May, the night skies are always clear. Along the grass, blue-green from the moonshine, there are dark shadows in the pomegranate trees and rosemary bushes where a person can hide away from the light of the moon. And under the oak tree. I stare at the shadows that it casts on the ground—a skeletal maze in the winter and billowing leaves in the spring.

The kitchen window shuts further down the house. My father is going to sleep. I don't try to find out if he and my mother have started to share the same bed again. They remind each other of him, and this damage can't be undone. I turn off my desk light and crawl into bed under the window. The moonlight falls on the sheets up to my waist. The rest of me hides in the shadows and watches the leaves move in the oak tree until I drift asleep.

For a whole week I watch her from my window. I bend over books and notes spilling over the bed from my schoolbag. There are flyers for parties I won't attend and unopened cards that old girlfriends have slipped into my locker because there are some words they can't say aloud. The sun is strong outside, and Julia sits in the grass, her legs stretched out. She reads, then leans back to stare into the light blue above and talk. She talks the most before dinner when she prepares to leave the oak tree for our silent house. She picks up her book and brushes the grass from her back, then looks around as if she is saying goodbye. Her mouth moves, and she smiles sadly, then walks back to the house.

At the end of the week, Julia starts baseball practice, so I go home for a few hours, but never leave the car. I turn off the engine and wait for the silence to come once the car has stopped settling. I sit in the driveway while the clouds grow dense above, and the rain begins to blur my view. Mom has started spending nights with her sister every Friday, although I know that if I called my aunt, she'd be home with the twins and no news from my mother. Mom will be at a bar downtown, or maybe a diner where she can order fries with her beer. I know that my mom in the diner window and my father at his office desk are looking out into the rain like me. I search through the running water for a clear view of our house, but I see nothing. I sit there staring until the hours have passed, and it's time to pick Julia up from school again.

Her outline forms in the distance. Her clothes are muddy and her curls are dripping and longer than usual. She opens the door. Raindrops linger on her eyelashes and fall from her nose.

You're late, I say.

She nods and wrings out her hair.

What are you doing?! It's getting all over the seat. I tug on her arm so she stops. She lets go of her hair and says nothing, staring forward out the window. She doesn't like yelling.

We drive in silence for a few lights.

What do you hear out there? I finally ask.

Julia turns and tilts her head at me.

In our backyard, I clarify.

Oh, she says, and she looks relieved like she understands something. Do you want to come out there with me?

No, I say quickly. I just want to know what you think you hear.

I turn on our street, and as the car slows, the falling rain grows loud. She is staring at me with her lips parted.

You think I'm crazy? Her voice is low and shakes a little.

Well, do you believe that you're hearing voices? I ask loudly.

Not voices. She doesn't say his name, but it fills the car.

I turn away from her and say, Right. Not voices. John. Who is dead.

The words hang between us until I pull into the driveway and unlock the doors. In a moment she is free of her seatbelt and out of the car. The rain weighs down her hair again, and she can hardly see me because water is hitting her face so fast.

It's where I hear him, Julia says. That's all I know.

She stares at me, then shuts the door and is gone. She runs along the side of the house through the gate to the back, and my hands fall so hard on the steering wheel that they hurt. The horn is loud, and the neighbors might come, so I let go and get out.

I move up the stairs into our extra room, lined with boxes and unfinished projects. I know where it is because the last time I searched this room, the dust left grey marks on my black clothes.

There is a wooden box beneath a cracked vase. I open the lid and it's fifth from the back, right where I left it on the day of his wake. I came up here to find it while the guests downstairs moved carefully around our family. I came up here searching for something to confirm my memories. To prove that when I was fourteen, I taught my six-year-old sister to hit a baseball without a tee. And though the photograph doesn't say it, John and I had agreed that this was important, and made her trust herself enough to hit the moving ball and abandon the plastic stand. My arm is outstretched, and Julia is readying to swing and the summer grass needs to be cut and we are sweating and swatting gnats, but moments after John took this picture she finally hit it.

And I know that John took the picture because when I pulled it out of this box two months ago at his wake, he looked up at me. His reflection in the glass door downstairs became a transparent foreground to the picture of Julia and me.

I fall to the dusty floor, knowing that I need a while to sit in the storage room with all the things we've forgotten. Julia is under her oak, wet and shivering in the rain, and I'm looking into his light eyes. We're left with so little. Work and a diner, an oak tree and a photograph. All trying to find him again.

You need to go to her and say you're sorry.

I know, I reply aloud.

Kathleen M. McCann/As If It Were Yesterday

Tomorrow will come
with its handful of snow
or full course.
Forecasters be damned.
Bearers of bad roads,
schedules undone.

In the early morning light,
from memory's bright purse,
Fore River's steep crane lords
over shipyard workers carding
in at the gate, lunch pails &
thermos tucked, wool caps snug.

And the collie. . .
asleep on the back stoop
beneath the peeling *Esso*
beyond the rotary &
its rotund granite ball.

Fifty years, like that.

Kathleen M. McCann/Second-Guessing Our Decision to Place My Mother on the Alzheimer's Unit

A gull keens the weight
of the world. So early

in the gray morning,
the smell of the sea

at the door. Last night
I dreamt a young girl

bundled tight, her mother
pulling her sled

up Wilson Avenue.
Roosevelt, Taft, Harding

all covered in fresh snow.
Jingle bells, jingle bells

the mother sings
and sings and sings

all the way home.

Kevin Rabas/Fall Up

Gunkle and I had this big mirror between us, hefting it
into the back of his blue pickup truck. Gunkle's part retarded,
a giant in blue jeans and green Crocs, wearing a white T-shirt
with battery acid on it. His glasses are thicker than my thumb.

So, we grab hold of this monster mirror, and it glints,
and we both look into that mirror, noticing the clarity
of that blue sky and those green oak leaves reflected
so perfectly that is appears you could just dive on into that mirror
and sink into the sky, and we think the same thing.
"You could fall up," Gunkle says, "and just keep on falling.
Nothing would stop you." And that was the way of it.
Gunkle's mind was now my mind, and I was in that mirror
falling on up through those white smoke clouds
headed towards an orange sun.

Gunkle and I stacked box bed springs on top the mirror,
and some branches from out front, and I could hear that large
    mirror crack,
but I think Gunkle and I could still see it—
that vision of sinking into sky, drowning
with only the sun to hold us up.

Kevin Rabas/Singing Muddy Waters at the Emporia Art Walk:

A Birthday Poem for Gary Holcomb

The sun is out in full today
for the first time in weeks,
radiating in hot wisps of gray on gray,
and we are on the sidewalk
outside Flint Hills Music,
our bassist behind the counter,
working the crowd.
So, it is just you and me.
Your blond guitar shines
against the sun, and my metal brushes
go hot in my hands. You have on
a straw Kangol hat and a black
T-shirt that says The Clash.
Next to us, under a sun tent,
Girl Scout cookies are sold.
"Shouldn't your drum be metal?"
one girl asks. Not in this sun.
You sing above the rush of traffic
that swishes by in schools. This street
could be filled with muddy water,
as it is months later in the flood,
but today the glint of the sun
is in our eyes, and the sky shines
white above us with only a hint
of turquoise blue, beckoning
blue, afternoon blues blue.
A frog in your throat, you work the crowd
with a gravelly voice, stopping
women on the sidewalk, some
with strollers, who stare.
You charm the crowd with the voodoo
verses of "Hoochie Coochie Man,"
including a black cat bone

and John the Conqueror.
On the sidewalk, in the shade,
as the song says, the pretty women
jump and shout, however now
clicking pictures as you sing,
"You got a boy-child comin',
Gonna be a son-of-a-gun,"
the call of the bluesman,
advertising his own birth.

Kate Martin Rowe/Death in South Dakota

The ground froze solid in winter. She died in winter,
so they couldn't bury her.

"Good night, Oma," the children would say on their way up to bed.

They kept thinking she would open her eyes,
spring up from the kitchen table and whip up a batch of cookies.

They didn't know what it means to live.

Some say she died missing
the old country,
but that's probably a lie to make things sadder.

Probably, her heart stopped
because she'd had a lot of difficult things to carry,
and it'd been a while.

The kitchen must have been warm, the body
must have ripened, the children must have known.

Kate Martin Rowe/What a Name Does for You

The landlord has begun painting, but we say
leave our fairy tale alone.
We are like the children who tried eating a house
and met a candied witch instead
(or was it a woman with a sweet disposition?).
We just want to go home.

The names in the paint catalog are rivers
in which to drown the unremarkable:
meadow, slate, ebony, jade.
Around here we strip off our skins
to unfold the bones underneath
because every year there are more names
to remember, people we love
who drop their well-being
like brass keys.
But terminology can't bring down a lavender sky,
which is where we're always
trying to get—

rents are climbing,
the bees have disappeared,
original toilets ripped out,
and scented roses too—and all we wanted
was a little peace of mind, colors
that wouldn't change names.

Alan Legrady/Tiles

Tictactoe underfoot.
One empty space hungry for more than it can eat,
No x or o left to appease an architect's appetite.
Last AVAILABILITY too big for the. . .
It won't fit.
Shadowy figures eclipsed by self-righteous light;
Night under the spacefiller,
A lid on a jar,
Restingwaiting to be disturbed,
Reproached to pieces by perturbed shadows.
Edges flush and corners cramped.

pieces enough to fill what is wanted to be filled.

the rest,

                                        discard.

fragments' puzzle fit cemented.

pieced, puzzle piece among a graveyard of puzzle pieces.

dissatisfaction.

blemish upon ugly design.

futile.

Linoleum asphyxiation, monotony's plague.

Krista Benjamin/Something about Morning

The stillness,
the radio's news,
the scent of rain. Something
about my neighbor,
picking up his newspaper,
in an orange plastic bag,
tossed on the step.
The cars all heading
this way or that,
a fine spray beneath
their wheels. Wet
pavement, and
something, too,
about the light
from the eastern
sun, slanting long,
as if there's all
the time in the world.

David Hovhannisyan/Masquerade

The constant talkers are the ones who hide,
compelled to mask their true identity,
disguised by words of arrogance and pride.

And can my heart untie the winding tide,
release my inner will unfearfully,
the constant talkers are the ones who hide.

A slight return to generate my guide,
I wish to find my flawless entity,
disguised by words of arrogance and pride.

Deceitful people masquerade untried,
creating speech towards obscenity,
the constant talkers are the ones who hide.

The thinker engineers his words inside,
continuing to keep his sanctity,
disguised by words of arrogance and pride.

And men of grace restrain themselves aside,
concealing secretive domains to flee,
the constant talkers are the ones who hide,
disguised by words of arrogance and pride.

Lyn Lifshin/The Mad Girl Loses Her Voice

as if trains ran
over her larynx,
splintering verbs
and grinding them into
the dust of the
lodestone in her dream.
It hurts to do
more than write the words.
Her fingers ache,
but she keeps on.
The phone's a gun.
She mouths an S.O.S.
behind frost on the stained glass,
window letters leaning up near
where her lips stick to glass,
doesn't understand when the
blind man doesn't answer.

Mark SaFranko/Satisfied, at Last

New York City. Helene Walker arrives from California to take a hot job at a telecommunications firm, in the same department where George Arkins happens to be working as a freelance writer of *Kiplingers*—global political and economic intelligence reports—for the executive staff. In those days George was full of disdain for the world of big business: he was going to be a writer, an artist along the lines of a Mailer or a Henry Miller. Of course, the rent had to be paid in the meantime, and the conventional remuneration made it possible for him to afford basement flats in places like Hoboken and Queens, and garrets in Jersey City and Brooklyn. In his free time, life was an adventure filled with women, bars and drugs—raw experience that was all going to be transformed one day into material. But Helene's arrival changed everything overnight. The attraction between them was immediate and mutual, and soon they were inseparable. Helene's softness was a haven after the tumult of George's love life—he was divorced once, after a young marriage, and had had scores of affairs and broken relationships. For Helene, George was someone with an edge, which was always attractive, not to mention that he was "creative," where she wasn't. But the thing that really did it for George was when Helene, over espresso in a Chelsea café, looked up at him after reading the first chapter of his latest attempt at a novel.

"What in the world are you doing working for that company? You have real talent!"

Though he was still relatively young at just over thirty, George had been waiting for years to hear those words. Helene's encouragement gave him the mystical impression that she would turn out to be extremely valuable to him, a person he could rely on to support his ambitions, because up to this point he had nothing to show for himself but a few manuscripts and a growing stack of impersonal rejection slips. And when some weeks later she suggested out of the blue that "you should come and live with me, let me worry about the practical realities like rent and food, while you concentrate on your art," their pact was sealed—and in the manner of mysterious events that have no explanation, their relationship took on its own peculiar form of life, and its strongest quality was an inexplicable endurance.

Within days of Helene's thumbs up to his writing, they were living under the same roof.

❖❖❖

George Arkins always assumed there had to have been men in Helene's life before they met; she was vivacious and alluring and had lived in Maine, Texas, San Diego, San Francisco and Santa Monica, so the state of California alone had to be littered with the detritus of her amatory past. She mentioned a Westwood businessman named Morris she'd had an on-and-off thing with, and a few other casual flings, most of which ended indifferently or unhappily, but her longest relationship was with someone in Los Angeles named Tod Standridge. Tod was a ringer for the Beatle George Harrison, and he worked as a production assistant and location manager for movie studios, including a legendary director's outfit in northern California. His goal was someday to be a producer. When he was involved with Helene, he did nothing but work twenty-four/seven. The frenetic behind-the-scenes activity of making motion pictures obsessed him for some reason she could never fathom—after hanging around a few sets and having an up-close look, she sized it up as a deadly snore, as well as superficial and empty. In the vast majority of cases, the results spoke for themselves. Nevertheless, and though Tod was nearly always out of town, they tried their best to make a go of it. He was, after all, a perfectly nice fellow, handsome, and so generous he'd give you the shirt off his back. In fact, they never seemed to break things off completely until she decided to take the job in New York. Before she left, he asked her to marry him. No, she decided: she was going to forge a new life for herself, let the past go altogether. When all was said and done, Tod was, well, *boring*, and so were the nuts and bolts of film production, despite what most people might think. There had to be more to life. She was determined to escape.

She said very little else about the guy to George. Tod Standridge remained a nebulous presence until one day a bouquet of roses arrived at the office. At first Helene thought they might be from George, but when he denied it, she grew pensive. He was standing next to her desk when she opened the attached card.

"Who from?"

"Actually, they're from Tod. . . ." Helene scanned the card, closed it, deposited it inside its envelope.

"So—what does he say?" George prodded gently.

"Oh. . . nothing." She seemed both wistful and uninterested in the gift at the same time. George knew enough to not press the issue. Things were going great guns between Helene and him. What threat could a man living three thousand miles away possibly pose?

But when Helene brought the flowers home that evening (at the time they were renting a brownstone in Park Slope, mostly on her salary) and installed them on the kitchen counter, George grew irritated.

"I'd rather not have to look at that stuff," he complained.

"But they're so pretty, don't you think? It would be a shame to waste them."

"No, it wouldn't. Who does this guy think he is to send you roses after all this time? What does he want, anyway?"

"It's obvious, isn't it?" She spoke the words rather dreamily.

George snorted. "Well, would you mind at least stashing them in your study so I don't have to see the damned things?"

"Oh come on, sweetie, take it easy. They don't mean a thing."

But without another word, Helene did as he requested. A few days later, when the flowers had withered and died, he watched sheepishly as she hauled them out to the trash.

"So what are you going to do? I mean about Tod?" he said when she joined him at the dinner table.

Her eyebrows arched with surprise. "Nothing. I'm in love with you."

❖❖❖

A few years later George married Helene on a Caribbean island during an extended autumn weekend. They traveled; George went on writing. For a long time not another word was uttered about Tod Standridge. Apparently he'd given up on Helene, and when George went through the mail there was never anything from the ex-boyfriend in California. As the exigencies of survival in New York took over—which they inevitably do—it was as if he'd never even existed.

George and Helene moved from Brooklyn to the Upper West Side, changed jobs, then changed jobs again. They accumulated the trappings of a shared life despite the fact that George was still struggling—indeed, was in a perpetual state of struggle—with his career, which never seemed to get off the ground despite the infrequent appearance of stories in literary quarterlies and a self-subsidized novel (which sank like a stone the week of its publication). In fact, George's battle was such that he'd come to entertain powerful doubts that he should ever have tried to write in the first place. As the years passed he often told himself that he should instead have become something more dignified and useful, like a teacher or a veterinarian, anything but persist in his pursuit of "self-expression."

"Sometimes I can't help feeling like I'm the biggest loser on the face of the earth," quipped George to his wife on more than one occasion. More than anything he detested having to think of himself as a pathetic "wannabe," one of those dull moths fluttering around the fringes of a glamor profession, who sees himself as more than he really is, especially when he flew out of the gate with such high expectations—but what else could he think?

"Nonsense. You've chosen a tough road. You've got to stay the course and realize you're in it for the long haul. Think of all the artists who've had to endure for decades to get their just due. Looks like you're going to be one of those. Don't feel sorry for yourself."

George tried to take her counsel to heart, but he was skeptical. "The myth of the misunderstood artist is just that, baby—a myth!" Moreover, where exactly was any evidence whatsoever that he *was* on the right track? The ugly truth was that were it not for his wife and her high-paying positions in the business world, George Arkins wouldn't even have had the wherewithal to spend any part of his time chasing a dream; he'd be busting his hump as a reporter in the hinterlands or teaching composition to freshmen at some second-rate college.

Worst of all was when someone who George had brushed shoulders with rocketed to overnight fame. Like Wayne Murphy, who'd landed a major publisher for his line of mediocre detective novels.

"I mean, could he really be so much more talented than me, Hel?"

"It's not a matter of talent and you know it. Look at what makes noise in the marketplace, Georgie. Just *look*. With the rare exception, it's the lowest common denominator. You're trying to do something more."

"Am I?"

But, of course, that was true, and she was right. Helene was always on target when it came to the crucial issues. And George would go back to his desk, to his latest novel that would never be published, or play fated not to be staged, and give it his best shot with a growing sense of resignation—or *defeat,* as it often felt to him. Moreover, an uneasy, guilt-ridden sense of deception had infested his spirit. These days he could scarcely justify thinking of himself in any other way than as a would-be, a fake.

Sometimes, when he and his wife were out of the city for the weekend, George found glum consolation in taking in the bewildering layers of milky stars in the night heavens: human beings, including himself, were nothing, they were more puny than the merest grain of sand on the beach. Nobody, including God probably, knew where we were, and, just as probably, nobody cared. It didn't much matter in the grand scheme who got to be successful, famous or rich, because when our brief time on earth was over, we were all going to be dead. Eventually, the human race itself, like the dinosaurs, would fade away.

❖❖❖

"You've never felt such a cold shoulder in your *life*!"

Helene had just gotten through recounting to her husband how she'd run smack into Tod Standridge's *mother*, of all people, in Macy's in Herald Square. Of course, she was the last person in the world she would ever expect to collide with, but there it was.

"I asked if she was here on a visit, she said yes, I asked how she was, she answered fine, conversation over. She was curt, with an edge of downright hostility. I was perfectly nice and all."

"I'm sure you were," George agreed, picking at the remains of his baked red snapper. By now so much time had passed since the incident of the roses that George felt nothing but curiosity at the mention of the Standridge name. "What do you make of it?"

"She wasn't too thrilled that I rejected her son, evidently. And evidently she has a long memory."

"So then what happened?"

"Nothing. She walked off without another word, not even a 'Nice seeing you after so long.' *Nothing*. It made me feel kind of—"

"What?"

"I don't know. Sad, I guess. Because it wasn't a bitter breakup between Tod and me. And I always got along with his family. But maybe he took it more seriously than I did after all."

"By the way, what do you figure he's up to nowadays?"

Helene shrugged. "God only knows."

"Think he's still a location manager—still in the business. . . ?"

"I wouldn't have the foggiest idea," said Helene, impaling a short stack of scalloped potatoes on her fork.

❖❖❖

It was a suffocating day in early August when George and Helene drove out to their storage bin in New Jersey, and, completely wilted from the vicious heat after struggling for a couple of hours with heavy cartons and furniture, decided to escape into the air-conditioned darkness of a movie theater. The nearest multiplex was offering *Africa*, one of those star-driven, mega-budget summer releases that George and his wife would never take in under normal circumstances (being aficionados of art-house films themselves), but since there wasn't much in the way of an alternative, they laid down their money and went inside.

From the first frame, *Africa* was a joke, and a very bad one at that. The plot and dialogue were ludicrous (rip-offs, George judged sourly, of those hackneyed 40s and 50s Saturday-matinee yarns in which the Great White Adventurer discovers a lost city overflowing with priceless treasure or brings 'em back alive), the acting by the attractive leads hammy, the artificial jungle beasts as phony-looking as badly printed counterfeit two-dollar bills. The flick was, in fact, so surprisingly cheesy for the hundred million it cost to make that the sight of bogus primates and reptiles incited hoots of derision, followed by gales of laughter, from the audience. One disgruntled patron even tossed an empty popcorn container at the screen—and this, no less, in the provinces, where such fare is presumably tolerated more readily than in the big city.

"*Jesus*, is this *shit!*" jeered the man in the seat next to George. "I demand a refund!"

"You said it," George sniggered. Nevertheless, the cool felt good on such a hellish day and he sank down into his seat and shut his eyes for a doze. He woke up just in time for the closing credits. The name "Tod Standridge" floated by, in the capacity of Production Manager.

"Look, George," blurted a surprised Helene.

"So—he's still in the business, after all," George said as they were walking out. "But let's face it—what dreck. Just god-*awful.*"

There wasn't much more to say about *Africa*. Even if George hadn't set the world on fire himself, there was some satisfaction in knowing that Tod Standridge was doing hack-work—even if he was getting paid handsomely for it.

George didn't know what in the world Helene might be thinking. He didn't ask.

❖❖❖

More time passed, but George's career remained stuck in neutral—more or less where it always was. But now there was a child, which complicated matters enormously: the birth of Carla meant that George's failures and shortcomings as artist *manque* were thrown into sharper relief. Having a daughter meant that he had to stay gainfully employed since there was another mouth to feed, and Helene wanted to spend more time with her baby and away from the workplace.

Still, he continued to poop along, banging away at his stories in the early mornings before reporting to work and whenever the meager time away from his duties (as an editor in a pharmaceuticals ad agency now) would permit. But there seemed to be a peculiar force working against his liberation from the mundane, let alone his success. After all this time and all his effort, the world still remained oblivious to George Arkins. He was well past forty.

Out of the corner of his eye George caught fleeting glimpses of Tod Standridge's erratic trajectory. After *Africa* there was another lengthy absence, then came *The Vestige*, a sci-fi thriller crammed with preposterous special effects, a film that garnered a batch of scornful reviews, lasted all of one week in the theaters, and vanished without a trace. What made it notable at all was the rise of Tod Standridge to *Co-Producer*, in conjunction with a pair of Spielberg stalwarts, a development that made George's heart lurch—with envy.

"I don't know whether you're aware of it, but your ex has taken another step up the ladder," he mentioned to Helene one night after they'd finally maneuvered their recalcitrant toddler into bed.

"My what?"

"Tod. Tod Standridge. That bomb, *The Vestige*? He was a muckety-muck on that one."

"The Vestige? That was him?. . . I hadn't been paying attention. God, I haven't thought of Tod Standridge in *such* a long time."

George's wife was tossing Carla's garments from one laundry basket to another in the bedroom. George was peeling off his shoes and socks.

"Any regrets?"

Helene was nonplused. "Over what?"

"That you didn't—well, you know."

"No, I don't."

"That you didn't stay in L.A. That you didn't stick it out with Tod."

He felt a little foolish asking the questions, but he had to.

"Don't be ridiculous."

"Still think you made the right choice?"

"There was no choice to be made. And if there was, the answer is yes."

❖❖❖

By now George Arkins was solidly into middle age. If he harbored any doubts about where he was in life, the white streaks in his hair and soft bulge above his belt were enough to persuade him. He continued to write, but the realization had long since set in that barring the one-in-one-hundred million miracle, he wasn't going to reach the Promised Land of Fame and Fortune. More and more often his work fell apart in his hands—stories and novels, even lousy ones, refused to congeal; what might burst into life with energy sputtered out within a few pages.

Meanwhile, things no longer went so smoothly for his wife, either. Whether it was the fact that her touch and looks (everyone knows they still count for something, even in the business world) had faded or her own luck had begun to slip, Helene lost one job, as manager of a consulting firm in mid-town, then another, as first assistant to the executive director of a grants foundation, in rapid succession. Her once-generous incomes were no longer there for George to rely on. With the arrival of a second child, they packed up and moved out of the city to an upstate suburb where their modest means made life with a growing family more affordable.

Tod Standridge helmed one or two other Hollywood productions, but since they suffered pretty much the same fate as *Africa* and *The Vestige*, their appearance didn't nettle George so much, though he did wince whenever he caught the name. Why was it, George wondered bitterly, that bomb after bomb, Tod was handed yet another chance, while he, after thirty years of dedicated work, still couldn't manage to grab the golden ring—or any ring? It was as if there were some inexplicable, absurd law of the universe at work which mandated that failure, perhaps even incompetence, on a grand scale should be rewarded, and the corollary was designed to keep diligent types like him from finding and holding even the most paltry audience. When he chewed on it, it made him furious, even outraged. But once the films went away, George would forget about Tod Standridge all over again.

❖❖❖

Then something appeared that George couldn't possibly ignore: a gargantuan two-page splash in the *Sunday Times* Entertainment section heralding the imminent opening of a new supernatural thriller called *The Second Dimension*, starring one of Hollywood's highest paid stars. . . Executive Producer, Tod Standridge.

George fumed. Tod Standridge had leaped another three steps up the ladder of power, this time to the very apex. As *executive* producer he was the big boss man, he pulled the performers' strings, he became the arbiter of America's shoddy taste. And he'd be the one standing at the podium at the Academy Awards next spring in the event *The Second Dimension* amounted to something commercially or critically. (Which, of course, was nothing but a remote possibility given Tod's track record.)

George announced the latest development to his wife, who was at first slightly piqued, then quickly apathetic.

"You're more interested in Tod Standridge than I ever was. His life has nothing to do with yours, George—you *do* understand that, don't you?"

But Standridge *did* have something to do with his life, in some way George couldn't explain, even to himself. He found himself hoping jealously, and with uncharacteristic pettiness, that *The Second Dimension* would suffer the fate of its predecessors and tank in a matter of days. But this time something much different was about to happen. The movie opened to generally poor, at best mixed reviews, but "word of mouth" was spreading a much different story. Everywhere, folks from secretaries to firefighters were talking about *The Second Dimension*; it seemed to have struck an invisible but universal chord (some critics pointed out by way of explanation that it was a rehash of the sappy new age super-hit of yesteryear, *Ghost*) and the crowds were flocking to see it. At the end of its first week of theatrical release it was number one. George could hardly believe it—after all of Tod Standridge's ignominious turkeys, he'd gotten insanely lucky and captured the goose that lays the proverbial golden egg.

Weeks two, three, four, and five of *The Second Dimension*'s run came and went, and when they were gone the movie was left standing in the same spot—at the top of the heap. More remarkably, it was the first film since *Titanic* to have done so, and it was showing signs of threatening that monster hit's record. Box office had topped one hundred and fifty million, and on hearing that tally George Arkins arrived at another distasteful epiphany—in addition to his staggering success, Tod Standridge had become a very wealthy man overnight.

When his curiosity finally got the best of him, George slipped out and took in a matinee; even the fact that *The Second Dimension* was nothing more than another heap of formulaic Tinseltown pap did nothing to make him feel better. He had fallen woefully short in his own aspirations and won the woman, while Tod Standridge had managed by some twist of fate to get everything George Arkins ever wanted out of life.

❖❖❖

Tod Standridge's amazing triumph preyed on George's mind night and day. When his little son called him a "stupid idiot" during an argument, he flashed for some inexplicable reason on the film producer. After work one evening he stopped into a bar for a drink, and, looking up at the TV screen, happened to catch Tod himself giving an interview to an entertainment reporter on the Oscar prospects for *The Second Dimension*. It was the first time George had ever set eyes on Standridge—he was well-dressed, youthful, and, most of all, brimming with confidence. George suddenly felt as if upstate New York was as far away as Borneo, and that he was stranded, and it depressed him out of all proportion to the reality at hand. It was as if he personally had been passed over.

Later that week he was in the produce section of the neighborhood A&P squeezing a Florida grapefruit when he overheard two workers, a teen-aged girl and an older man who were unloading crates of apples, discussing *The Second Dimension*.

"Oh my *God*—was that *incredible?*" gushed the girl. "My favorite movie *ever!* Of all *time!*"

"Wasn't it?" answered her partner. "My wife couldn't stop crying. And when it turned out that the husband was *dead*—what a shock! I never saw it coming!"

George couldn't help butting in. He objected that the movie was shit, and that he knew in the first ten minutes what was going to happen. The workers' eyes widened. They ceased stacking fruit. When George added, "My wife's ex-boyfriend was the executive producer of *The Second Dimension*," they looked at him as if he were certifiable.

❖❖❖

"I want you to call him."

It was nine o'clock, a Monday night, late September. The kids had finally stopped screeching and bickering and were asleep, and George and his wife were in front of the TV with their drinks, Helene, herbal tea, George, a beer. He'd been drinking far too much lately, and tonight was no exception. It had been a rather somber evening in the Arkins household because George had been let go that day from his latest job. The development was completely unexpected. Business was off and there was one too many editors on the payroll—somebody had to go. A brief commercial spot for *The Second Dimension* had just flitted across the screen. For George Arkins, it was the last straw.

George muttered it again, as if to himself: "I want you to call him."

Helene, startled, stared at her husband. "What in the world are you talking about?"

"Tod. Tod Standridge."

"Oh, God. You're not still riding that tired horse, are you, George?"

George glanced at his wife. "You understand what's happened here, don't you? You understand that you could be lounging in a mansion on the beach in Malibu, with millions in the bank, never having to work another day in your life, instead of sitting in the middle of nowhere with some fuck-up struggling to make ends meet? You *do* understand that, don't you?"

George wasn't laughing. He was coming apart at the seams.

"It's crossed my mind, yes."

It was the first time Helene went along with her husband when the subject of Tod was brought up, though she did so with a bit of smirk; to her it had become a kind of perverse joke.

"But George, sweetheart—get real here. There's more to life than someone else's success."

George shook his head. "I know where he is. I pulled the information off the net at work one day when I couldn't get the bastard off my mind. Brontosaurus Pictures, Universal City. He's got an office on the lot. Office, hell—after what this movie did, he must have his own *compound*. I'll get the number for you."

George pushed himself off the sofa and went for the telephone. Helene watched him, convinced that her husband had to be playing some kind of wacky prank, and that she simply wasn't catching on.

"Very funny, George. Very funny." She actually laughed.

"I'm not joking around here, Helene. I'm dead serious."

She listened in consternation as he contacted information. "Connect me, go ahead, please."

"This is too much now. Really, George. And I want you to cut down on your drinking, starting right now."

"Tod Standridge's office," George was saying across the room. "Yes, I'll hang on." He took another long swig of his beer.

Helene got up. "I'm going to bed, George. I can't be bothered with such stupid—"

George leaped across the room to block her way to the staircase.

"You're being absolutely ridiculous, George! What in the world's gotten *into* you? What are you trying to *prove*?"

"Don't you get it? Don't you fucking *get* it, Helene? I can't prove *anything!* In thirty long years I've been able to prove *nothing*, not one, single miserable thing!" He glowered at her as if she were his mortal enemy, responsible for everything that had ever gone wrong in his life. *"It didn't work, don't you get it?* You and I didn't work! We *jinxed* each other! You should have stayed in L.A. and left me alone! It was your fault—you!"

By now a woman's silky but business-like voice had begun speaking at the other end of the line.

"*Hello?* Can I help you? Is something wrong?"

The sound seemed to bring George to his senses, and he stared at the receiver as if he couldn't figure out what it was doing in his hand.

Helene stepped forward and took it gingerly away from her husband as if it were a gun.

"We dialed the wrong number. Sorry," she said into the mouthpiece. Then she turned her brimming eyes to her husband. "Oh, George," she sighed.

A half-smile appeared on her lips. "Are you working on something? A story, maybe?"

George shook his head.

"Go to bed, George. And when you wake up in the morning, start something new. You can do it, George. I know you can."

CONTRIBUTORS NOTES

Phyllis Carol Agins has written two novels, short fiction, a children's book, and an architectural study. She happily divides her time between Philadelphia and Nice, France.

Nancy Aldrich has taught secondary and college English and has been an executive director for a chamber music society in Portland, Maine, where she lives. Her poems have appeared in *Tar River Poetry*, *Willow Review*, and *The Chaffin Journal*.

Joanne Allred has published two collections of poems, *Whetstone* (Flume Press) and *Particulate* (Bear Star Press). She lives on a few acres in a canyon outside Chico, California.

John Azrak was the English chair of a secondary school for twenty years. He has recently published or has work forthcoming in *Poetry East*, *Court Green*, *The Bryant Review*, and *The Hawaii Pacific Review*.

Stuart Bartow lives in Salem, New York, and teaches writing and literature at Adirondack Community College. He also chairs the Battenkill Conservancy. His collection *Reasons To Hate The Sky* will be published by Word Press later this year.

Lory Bedikian earned her MFA in Poetry from the University of Oregon, where she received the Dan Kimble First Year Teaching Award in Poetry.

Gayle Jansen Beede bikes to work as surgical coordinator at a small hospital. For seven years, she edited poetry for *ART/LIFE*.

Krista Benjamin lives in Carson City, Nevada. Her poems and stories appear in *The Best American Poetry 2006*, *Margie*, *Minnesota Review*, *Pearl*, and *Chiron Review*.

Michael Boccardo resides in High Point, North Carolina, and has poems published in *Hayden's Ferry Review*, *Rattle*, *The Bitter Oleander*, and *Kakalak*. Currently, he is a part-time student.

Nancy Botkin's full-length collection, *Parts That Were Once Whole*, is available from Mayapple Press. She has been published in *Poetry*, *Poetry East*, *The Midwest Quarterly*, and *The South Dakota Review*. She lives and teaches in South Bend, Indiana.

John Brantingham's work has appeared in Garrison Keillor's *Writer's Almanac*, *The Journal*, *Tears in the Fence*, and *Pearl*. His latest chapbook, *The Mediterranean Garden*, is forthcoming from Finishing Line Press. He teaches English at Mt. San Antonio College.

Teresa Breeden is an Ash Canyon Poet and a NV Fellowship winner. Her publications include *California Quarterly*, *Mid-American Poetry Review*, *Ruah*, and *Snowy Egret*.

Randall Brown teaches at Saint Joseph's University and holds an MFA from Vermont College. Recent work has appeared or is forthcoming in *Cream City*, *Hunger Mountain*, *Connecticut Review*, *Saint Ann's*, *Evansville Review*, *Dalhousie*, and *upstreet*. He is the author of *Mad to Live* (Flume Press, 2008).

Susan Howard Case received her MFA from Bennington in June, 2007, and lives in Leverett, Massachusetts. She leads poetry workshops for children and adults and has had poems published in *The Comstock*

Review, The Ledge, Peregrine, Primavera, The Sow's Ear, and *Small Pond Magazine.*

Susana H. Case has recent work in *Cider Press Review, Coe Review, Diner,* and *Gulf Stream Magazine.* She is the author of *The Scottish Café* (Slapering Hol Press, 2002) and *Anthropologist In Ohio* (Main Street Rag, 2005).

Crystal Charee lives and works in Glendale. She is a part-time Glendale College student who studies creative writing.

Patricia Clark teaches at Grand Valley State University in Michigan. She is the author of two books of poetry: *My Father on a Bicycle* and *North of Wondering.* Her poetry has appeared in *The Atlantic Monthly, Slate, Poetry,* and *The Gettysburg Review.*

Doug Cox was born and raised amongst the strip-malls, grapevines, and salvage yards of Fresno, California. He studied poetry and punk rock at Cal Poly SLO, holds an MFA from Indiana University, and is currently finishing up his PhD at Florida State. His recent work has appeared or is forthcoming in *Apalachee Review, Poetry Southeast,* and *Rio Grande Review.*

Mary Christine Delea is originally from Long Island and now lives in Oregon. She is the author of two chapbooks and one full-length collection of poetry, *The Skeleton Holding Up the Sky* (Main Street Press). She has a PhD in English, but is currently taking a break from academia to be a stay-at-home writer and quilt designer.

Mary R. Estrada was born in Iowa and lived in San Francisco before moving to Los Angeles. After retirement, she returned to college to complete a degree in Spanish and study creative writing at Glendale College.

Kimberly K. Farrar currently resides in Astoria, New York. She has a BA in Creative Writing from the University of Arizona and an MA in TESOL from Hunter College. Her work has been published in *Long Shot*, *Lullwater Review*, *Mudfish*, and *The Ledge*.

Bart Galle is a medical educator and artist who has published a letterpress book of paintings and poems, *Continuing Presence* (2004). His poems have appeared or are forthcoming in *White Pelican Review*, *Main Channel Voices*, and *Coe Review*.

Jill Gerard lives on the bank of a tidal creek in Wilmington, North Carolina. Her first chapbook of poems, *Something Yet Unseen*, was published by Finishing Line Press. She edits *Chautauqua*, the literary journal sponsored by Chautauqua Institution. Her poems have appeared in *Comstock Review*, *PMS*, *Blueline*, *Hawaii Pacific Review*, *Ars Medica*, and *Soujourn*.

Phyllis Grilikhes' recent book is *To Set A Light In Every Tunnel*. She is a former dancer and an active musician and teaches psychology at City College of San Francisco.

Aaron Hellem lives in Leverett, Massachusetts, where he attends the MFA Program for Poets and Writers at the University of Massachusetts Amherst and serves as managing editor of the *Massachusetts Review*. His short stories have recently appeared in *Ellipsis*, *Menda City Review*, *13th Warrior*, *Oklahoma Review*, *Beloit Fiction Journal*, and *Confluence*.

David Hovhannisyan was born in Yerevan, Armenia. He is a creative writing student at Glendale College and an introspective painter.

Brian Johnson is the author of *Self-Portrait* and *Torch Lake and Other Poems*. His work has appeared in *American Letters and Commentary*, *The*

Prose Poem: An International Journal, Quarter after Eight, Sentence, and *Connecticut Review*.

Nancy Kassell's poems have been published in *Willow Springs, Salamander*, and *Kalliope*. She lives in Brookline, Massachusetts.

Lewis S. Keith is a retired CPA with both undergraduate and graduate degrees. He also has studied creative writing at Glendale College. He continues writing from Carillon, a retirement community in Lubbock, Texas.

Arin Keshishian is a creative writing student at Glendale College, hoping to build a career as a community college professor teaching cultural anthropology and history. He currently works with elementary school children in an afternoon child day care center. He lived in southern France prior to moving to the United States.

Hari Bhajan Khalsa is a Life Coach and workshop facilitator. Her time is split between the sprawling city of Los Angeles and the little mountain town of Sisters, Oregon. Her work has been published, or is forthcoming, in *Fulcrum, New York Quarterly, Roanoke Review, Tiger's Eye, Schuylkill Valley Journal*, and *Phantasmagoria*.

Brandon Krause is an English major at Glendale College who plans to transfer to California State University, Northridge.

Alan Michael Yoshio Legrady currently lives in Glendale and attends Glendale College. He aspires to teach English in Japan.

Janice Lierz dreamed of becoming a traveling troubadour but veered into a twenty-year career as an executive with Fortune 500 companies. As entrepreneur and artist, she has returned to her tie-dyed dreams as a poet and CEO of a nonprofit organization that grants residency fellowships to emerging writers, poets, and painters.

Lyn Lifshin is the author of *Another Woman Who Looks Like Me*, *The Licorice Daughter: My Year With Ruffian*, *Before It's Light*, *Cold Comfort*, *Desire*, *Persephone*, *92 Rapple Drive*, *Nutley Pond*, and *Lost in the Fog*.

Joanne Lowery's poems have appeared in *Birmingham Poetry Review*, *Smartish Pace*, *Eclipse*, *Atlanta Review*, and *Poetry East*. She lives in Michigan.

Curtis Luckey studied creative writing at Glendale College before transferring to Cal State University Northridge. He is pursuing a degree in English and a teacher's credential.

Kathleen McCann lives in Weymouth, Massachusetts, and teaches poetry and American literature at Eastern Nazarene College in nearby Quincy. Her chapbook, *The Sea's Rosary*, is published by Timberline Press.

Kathleen McGookey earned degrees from Hope College and Western Michigan University and has taught at those institutions and at Interlochen Center for the Arts. Her poems, prose poems, and translations have appeared in *The Antioch Review*, *Boston Review*, *Epoch*, *Field*, *Indiana Review*, *The Laurel Review*, *Ploughshares*, *The Prose Poem: An International Journal*, *Quarterly West*, *Seneca Review*, *West Branch*, and *Willow Springs*. Her book is *Whatever Shines* (White Pine Press). She lives in Michigan.

Schubert Moore's work has appeared in *Confrontation*, *Sanskrit*, *Poem*, *Pearl*, *The Palo Alto Review*, and *The Mad Poets Review*. He has taught at the college level and is a committed cook and fishing boat captain.

Scott Owens' second book of poems, *The Fractured World*, is published by Main Street Rag. He is the author of a previous collection, *The Persistence of Faith*.

Carla Panciera has published fiction, memoir, and poetry in *The Chattahoochee Review*, *Nimrod*, *The New England Review*, *The Sycamore Review*, *Under the Sun*, *Kalliope*, and *Painted Bride*. Her collection of poetry, *One of the Cimalores*, received the Cider Press Book Award and was published in 2005. She lives in Rowley, Massachusetts.

Cully Pappas has lived in New York, Massachusetts, and Georgia. She has returned to Glendale College after 25 years to study creative writing. She is currently a realtor in Los Angeles.

James Pate grew up in Memphis. He received an MFA from the Writers' Workshop at the University of Iowa, and his fiction has appeared in *Black Warrior Review*, *Blue Mesa Review*, and *New Delta Review*. He currently lives in Chicago.

Mary Bass Poulin teaches English at Carrabassett Valley Academy, a college preparatory ski/snowboard academy in Maine, and has an MFA from Vermont College. Her work has been included in New England regional journals, such as *The Café Review* and *The Stolen Island Review*.

Donna Pucciani has published poems in *International Poetry Review*, *Mid-America Poetry Review*, *Valparaiso Poetry Review*, and *Spoon River*. Her books include *The Other Side of Thunder* (Flarestack, 2006), *Jumping Off the Train* (Windstorm, 2007) and *Chasing the Saints* (Virtual Artists Collective, 2008).

Kevin Rabas teaches creative writing and literature at Emporia State University, co-directs the creative writing program, and is co-editor of

Flint Hills Review and Bluestem Press. His first book of poetry, *Bird's Horn and Other Poems*, was released by Coal City Review Press.

Susan Richardson's poems, stories, and articles have been published or are forthcoming in *Fiction International, Women. Period., The Dos Passos Review*, and *One for the Road*. She is the founding editor of Winterhawk Press.

Richard Robbins was raised in California and Montana. His recent poetry collections include *Famous Persons We Have Known* and *The Untested Hand*. He currently directs the creative writing program and Good Thunder Reading Series at Minnesota State University, Mankato.

Kate Martin Rowe teaches composition at Glendale College and Los Angeles City College, and her writing has appeared in *The Beloit Poetry Journal, The California Quarterly*, and *The Northridge Review*. She lives near downtown Los Angeles.

Mark SaFranko is a novelist, short story writer, playwright, and actor. His novel *Hating Olivia* was published by Murder Slim Press.

Cassie Schmitz currently lives in Tallahassee, Florida, where she graduated with a BA from Florida State University.

Daniel Shalvardzhyan is a creative writing and drama student at Glendale College. He is also an avid member of the debate team who is pursuing a career in acting. He plans to transfer to Cal State Northridge in the fall.

Donald Sheehy is a Professor of English at Edinboro University of Pennsylvania. He has published extensively on the life and work of Robert Frost.

Askold Skalsky has published poems in *Southern Poetry Review* and *Notre Dame Review*. He has recently received a prize for poetry from the Maryland State Arts Council. This is his second appearance in *Eclipse*.

Jeffrey Talmadge is a graduate of Duke University, The Warren Wilson College MFA Program for Writers, and the University of Texas School of Law. A full-time musician, he records for Corazong Records and tours in the United States and Europe. Originally from Texas, he now lives in the Atlanta area.

Jacqueline Tchakalian, a visual artist as well as a poet, is a former co-director of Valley Contemporary Poetry Series and a current member of the organizing committee of the Los Angeles Poetry Festival.

Sheila Tombe was the 2006-2007 recipient of the South Carolina Arts Commission Poetry Fellowship. She was poet in residence at Brookgreen, Pawley's Island. She is from Belfast, Northern Ireland, and teaches at the University of South Carolina Beaufort.

Jessica Treadway is the author of *Absent Without Leave*, a collection of stories, and *And Give You Peace*, a novel. Her stories have appeared in *The Atlantic, Ploughshares, The Hudson Review, Glimmer Train, Five Points*, and *Agni*. She lives outside Boston.

Austin Tremblay currently teaches at New Mexico State University, where he is earning an MFA. His work has been featured, or is forthcoming, in *Lullwater Review, California Quarterly, Touchstone*, and *Pembroke Magazine*.

Helen Wickes's first book of poems, *In Praise of Landscape*, was published by Sixteen Rivers Press in 2007. She lives in Oakland, California, where for many years she worked as a psychotherapist. She received her MFA from Bennington College.

Rolf Yngve served over 35 years in the Navy as a practitioner in Surface Warfare. During the 1970s his work appeared in *Quarterly West, Greensboro Review, Best American Short Stories, 1979,* and *Sudden Fiction.* He now writes fulltime. "Billy" is his first published work since 1982.

Emily Ann Zietlow lives and works in Los Angeles. She received a BA in creative writing from the University of Southern California, where she was managing editor for the online journal, *AngeLingo.*